P9-CBQ-727

HOW TO
FIGHT THE
DRUG MENACE

Henry L. Adams

Family of Faith Library

WILLIAM S. GARMON
AND PHIL STRICKLAND

HOW TO FIGHT THE DRUG MENACE

BROADMAN PRESS
Nashville, Tennessee

© Copyright 1970 • Broadman Press
All rights reserved
422–543

Where personal opinions are expressed
they are the opinions of the authors. The content
of this Broadman book is not to be taken
as the official position of the
Southern Baptist Convention

Dewey Decimal Classification Number: 178
Library of Congress Catalog Card Number: 76–117300
Printed in the United States of America
21.5My70KSP

PREFACE

Every major civic group in the United States this year has given some attention to what is termed the "drug problem." Almost every day during the week some one of the mass media carries a story about the death of a young person from an overdose of drugs; college or high school youths and drug use; hippies and drugs; or the arrest of someone trafficking in marijuana, pills, or heroin. Politicians, parents school officials, and church leaders are concerned. Even the young themselves are in large numbers attempting to find reliable information and sympathetic adults with whom they can discuss the problem.

There is no question that drug abuse is a problem, but there is lack of agreement on its extent, its nature, and the possible solutions. This book does not solve all of the problems, but it is written to help parents, church, and community leaders find solutions. It is intended to inform, persuade, and move to action. Major attention is given to the question of why the young are seemingly willing to try anything once; to abuse of chemical comforts on the part of young and old; and to the use of marijuana, LSD, and heroin. Since the laws relating to drug use are under attack, especially the laws relating to marijuana, a chapter is devoted to the legal issues. Perhaps most important of all, an effort is made to give guidance to parents and church leaders who are interested in a program of drug-abuse education.

Some of my chapters in this book are a revision of materials written originally as curriculum materials for John Hendrix, Editor, Adult Section, Church Training Department, The Sunday School Board of the Southern Baptist Convention. He has graciously consented to the use of these materials in this form.

Phil Strickland was asked to join the senior author in this project because of his unique qualifications. He is an attorney and has had extensive experience in drug-abuse education in his capacity as a staff member of the Christian Life Commission, Baptist General Convention of Texas.

Appreciation should be expressed to many people for assistance, but for the most part they must remain unnamed. The footnotes give credit to publishers for use of the materials indicated. The Associated Press should be cited for special commendation.

WILLIAM S. GARMON
April, 1970

CONTENTS

1

THE LURE
OF FORBIDDEN FRUIT

(By William S. Garmon)

The writer of Proverbs said, "Stolen waters are sweet, and bread eaten in secret is pleasant" (Prov. 9:17). Apparently forbidden fruit has always been an attraction. However, what is forbidden may vary with time, place, and culture. The forbidden and the accepted are more or less culturally defined.

The lure of forbidden fruit is something of a problem to people of all age levels, but it is probably at its highest intensity when compounded with the natural rebellion of youth. The problem is further complicated in present-day society because there is no real place in our society for young people. They are welcomed as sports figures and as consumers, but otherwise there is a tendency to want them out of the way. The economy cannot absorb them into the work force. Therefore they are kept in school as long as possible or channeled into the military. They are discouraged from establishing families until accepted into the work force. Participation in the body politic is not permitted in a meaningful way; however, currently there is some real possibility that this will change.

Just what is the real role the young are permitted to play in our society? Should we be surprised when they seek diversion,

9

something to amuse, kill the time, or give meaning to existence? That there is a teenage subculture or even a young people's subculture in the United States is hardly to be doubted, nor should it come as a surprise to us. There is always something of a generation gap in that each new generation is socialized at a different point in time. Even the youngest child in a large family has parents who are quite different from those of the eldest. The values of one generation are passed along to the next, but never without undergoing some testing. Behavior patterns are learned, whether these patterns are socially accepted or characterized as deviant behavior. As a general rule, children reflect the values of the older generation, but with some modification. At times it is to be expected that the young will reject the values of the

---

NEW YORK (AP)—Police arrested three boys they say were peddling heroin on Mermaid Ave. in the Coney Island section of Brooklyn. They say the boys—ages 11, 13 and 15— are not users, just pushing after school for profit. (Associated Press, January 29, 1970.)

---

older generation outright. Young people the world over will pursue a pattern of life which is found satisfying in some way. This satisfaction may be real or imagined, tangible or intangible. Why do they act this way?

Standing on Father's Shoulders

As distinct from the animal kingdom, the human young begin life by inheriting a highly developed culture. Each generation does not start over for itself, but begins with a culture transmitted by parents, other significant adults, and peers. The whole concept of human involves not just a biological inheritance, but a social and cultural environment as well. It is an error to fall into the trap of either environmental or biological determinism. Suffice it to state at this juncture that biological inheritance sets severe limits on the relative value of environmental factors for good or for ill. The converse is also true. Potentiality, however great, is rarely realized apart from an environment which encourages the fullest development of the potential. It follows that a rich environment cannot overcome an inherited low mental capacity.

The family plays a major role in shaping personality and in the transmission of the culture. This is the socialization process. Psychologists indicate that most of our basic attitudes toward life are shaped in the very early years of life. Therefore the home is extremely important to religion, government, the educational system, the moral fabric of society, and all social institutions. The patterns set in the home and the basic groundwork done here have a tremendous influence on the subsequent involvement or lack of involvement of the child in the social world. The child learns the folkways, mores, norms, values, and to some extent the legal standards of his society in the socialization process. He learns love, hate, concern, apathy—attitudes. Young people tend to reproduce in their own homes the basic style of life they experienced as children. In other words we tend to repeat the culture we inherit, although at times a child rebels and rejects, at least in part, the inherited cultural patterns. This rejection is not usually total, but selective. Children quickly detect the difference between profession and practice. The pattern the young tend to repeat will be the actual practice

11

of the older generation rather than the pattern of life the adults profess to be following. We are imperfect teachers, and it is good that we are because there are many aspects of our cultural life which should be destroyed.

What happens to a child brought up in a subculture which is characterized by normlessness or in some cases by a set of values which not only reject the values of the dominant society, but directly oppose them? A child growing up in an urban slum, for example, rarely learns the middle class virtue of deferred gratification, but lives in a world of now. It is not strange at all that the child of a third-generation welfare recipient is not highly motivated to work. The child's value structure is shaped largely by his social environment. What models does he have? What heroes are presented to him? If a child receives brownie points from his peers for building a better zip gun rather than for going to church or running errands for the druggist down the block, then don't be surprised when you can't enlist him in Sunday School or the Boy Scouts. Unfortunately—or is it fortunately?—we learn most of our do's and don't's from parents and peers. Morality, manners, modesty, and values are all largely relative to the culture. For example, the rules of modesty in our society require women to cover their breasts. However, in some parts of the world, as a matter of tradition, women do not cover their breasts. The only persons who would consider them immodest would be foreign visitors.

Cultural patterns once established have an amazing amount of vitality and strength. One of the reasons prohibition of the sale of alcoholic beverages did not work in the United States was because regular consumption of alcoholic beverages was a part of the cultural fabric of many of the ethnic groups who

GROSSE POINTE, Mich. (AP)—A random survey indicates that half of the 1,000 high school seniors in this exclusive Detroit suburb, where many wealthy officials of the auto industry live, have used illegal drugs at least once.

"It's definitely time that our parents become aware that their boys and girls are no longer just playing jacks down in the basement," said school superintendent Theos Anderson. (Associated Press, January 14, 1970.)

made up the population of the country. Alcoholic beverages were culturally approved in some groups just as they carried a taboo in others.

Could the drug problem be solved by changing the laws and making what is now forbidden permissible? It would seem that this is the answer proposed even by some learned social scientists. It is said that marijuana is the drug of the young, whereas alcohol is the drug of the old. If the older generation is permitted its booze, then, the argument goes, permit the younger generation to have its "pot." There are some errors in the argument. Interestingly enough the situation seems to be reversed in India. The young there will have nothing to do with "hash" for this is the drug of the old. In the United States no group, even the youth subculture, wholly approves of the use of marijuana, and this is not the case with alcohol. However, one is made to wonder if alcohol or even tobacco would have ever been made legal had our forefathers known the personal and social consequences of long-term abuse of these substances.

Becoming Adult

Adults often forget just how difficult it is to grow up. They forget their struggles—their foolhardy acts. Or maybe they do not forget enough. Sometimes they fear that their children are doing all those things they did and more. One has to wonder

---

VATICAN CITY (AP)—The Vatican daily yesterday condemned the spreading wave of drug-taking as "an industry of a new moral enslavement" and called on "the honest and moral majority" to stop it. (Associated Press, March 22, 1970.)

---

about whether or not today's parents would fare as well in the modern complex world as teenagers as today's dynamic youth are doing. As a whole they cope quite well.

Self-identity is a constant search for youth. Really, it goes on into the adult years. However, self identity as an individual apart from the family and the group begins to emerge at some point in adolescence. The person comes to know himself as a self only as he becomes aware of others as separate individuals. The diverse options or varied life styles possible for the young in our highly developed society add to the problem of self-identity. At some point in development, however, the self is perceived as probably the most important of all social values which exist.

Mental maturity progresses to the point in adolescence that questions are raised about the inherited life styles. Moral patterns will not only be questioned, but they will be tested. Inconsistencies between what the establishment professes to believe and what is actually practiced will be noted in particular. The practice of the elders will be copied as a rule rather than the codes which are taught. Charges of hypocrisy will be made.

14

Negative feelings will come to the fore. Yet the young will tend to follow the significant adults in their lives—to follow their practice, that is. Drug use is an excellent example. Whereas cigarettes and alcohol were the forbidden fruits for the middle-aged, drugs which are becoming increasingly available are the major, but by no means the only, forbidden fruit for today's youth. The use of marijuana by the young is almost a direct mimicry of the adult pattern in the use of alcohol.

The rebellion of modern youth has been reported in depth as if it were a new phenomenon; it isn't. It is the nature of the young to destroy that which is old and to build that which is

---

NORTH MIAMI BEACH, Fla. (AP)—Hours after his father emotionally pleaded for help in creating a youth center to combat drug abuses, the son of a city councilman was arrested on a charge of selling heroin. (Associated Press, February 12, 1970.)

---

new. In fact these are the cultural heroes who go out to fight the dragons, the dragons being the old cultural patterns of the past. In the romantic stories of fiction, the dragon is always dispatched, he never wins. In the real world he does win, for young men grow old and cease to go forth to do battle.

The mass media have done an excellent job of informing us about the generation gap, the challenge to the establishment. The result is that many people are convinced that this is new. In reality it is only more intense and extensive than ever before in history. Rapid social change is the mark of our age. It is difficult, however, to distinguish between the delinquent and the rebel, the hero and the villain. In an era when change is so rapid and intense, there is difficulty in keeping the social fabric intact. The difference between values and practice become glaring. Everything seems to be in a state of flux.

Learning to be an adult is not an easy task, and it seemingly becomes more difficult as society becomes increasingly more complex. Striving to be free from parental influence and authority has always been a part of the emerging pattern of independence in our society. In societies where the extended family dominates the young, this will not be true; there will be little challenge to parents. In our society rebellion, the testing of boundaries, the search for limits will be aimed at both parents and authority in general. It is difficult to discern whether this lashing out is a desire to hurt the parent, a search for security, a cry for definite limits to be set, or identification with the peer group. The young themselves do not know, for like the adults they tend to operate from mixed motives.

How important is the peer group? This question is difficult to answer and could be handled with more ease if the exact age group were indicated; however, the peer group tends to become increasingly important as the child grows more and more toward maturity. There are times when the desire to be a part of the group and to have the approval of the group becomes more important than the family. This is particularly true if the developing child is cut off from interaction with significant adult models. With increasing urbanization and more marked separation of home life and work life, the growing child has limited opportunity to observe adults in their roles. The only recourse is to depend more heavily upon the peer group for support. However, it is quite rare for children or young people to rebel completely against parents; usually they continue to care what parents think. Eventually the moral values and life style of the parents become, with some modification, the values and life styles of the children.

The Lure

Human behavior is complex and motivation behind behavior is usually more so. The lure of forbidden fruit to the young cannot be explained simply by resorting to labels such as: a desire for kicks, rebellion, or even deviant behavior. Much

---

COLLEGE PARK, Md. (AP)—More than one-third of the University of Maryland students taking part in a poll said they have smoked marijuana.

The survey of 600 students showed an increase of from 15 per cent in 1967 to a new figure of 35.6 per cent.

Furthermore, 25.4 per cent of the students polled said they intend to continue using the drug. (Associated Press, January 15, 1970.)

---

behavior is influenced by the ongoing process of development. Few people, adults or young persons, act rationally at all times or even most of the time. W. I. Thomas has said that man wishes for four things: security, recognition, response, and new experience. No one does anything without some reason or drive behind the action. How much behavior is motivated by organic drives and how much by acquired drives may be impossible to determine. As a general rule, however, most human behavior is oriented toward some type of reward. Behavior, then, particularly among the immature, tends to be basically gratification-oriented.

Man wants to be a part of a group, to be accepted, liked, and loved. Young people usually desire both love and friendship from both parents and peers. The herd instinct—a desire to be a part of something, the we feeling—is rarely absent. Therefore, many of our actions are predicated upon obtaining group approval. Being accepted by the group as a regular fellow may entice a young man to join in smoking a joint of marijuana, drinking an alcoholic beverage, or engaging in an overt act of delinquency. The rewards of the euphoric or depressant action of the chemical may be incidental. The material reward from the theft by a juvenile gang may not be nearly so important as being given recognition by the leader of the gang.

Problem-solving and running risks are apparently inherently rewarding. Men need variety and adventure in life. Young people want challenge and stimulation. They shun boredom like the plague. They refuse to live in a static world. How else do we explain some of their actions? Why do men climb mountains and explore caves? Because they are there. How do we explain the desire of some men to risk their lives driving racing automobiles or flying jet planes? The astronauts are the current heroes. Many men would like to go to the moon, while others are content to make new discoveries in science and medicine. Yet they are nonetheless challenged. Why does the military enlist or draft young men? It is not just for their strength and vigor, but because they will dare to take a chance, to venture, or maybe even to be foolhardy.

Someone protests, "Self-preservation is nature's first law." Well, yes and no. It is true that the instinct for survival is

WASHINGTON (AP)—Good grief. Old Charlie Brown a glue sniffer?

It looks that way. After all, Charlie's got the bottle in his hand when the "Peanuts" gang confronts him. But then he holds up the model plane he's working on. "What a blob, getting us all excited," says Lucy in disgust. And Snoopy wonders: "Why do they call it dope?"

That scene, or others like it, will begin appearing on television screens this year as the Advertising Council—with the blessing of the White House—begins an "unsell campaign" on drugs aimed at children 7 to 12 years. (Associated Press, February 12, 1970.)

---

present in the human animal, but not to the exclusion of the love for adventure. Man does seek security, a place to find seclusion when the going gets rough, or it may be simply a desire to know someone cares. Meaning, purpose, and the desire for adventure are interwoven in the human spirit. The psychological precondition to destructiveness or creativity is anxiety. How can the desire for adventure, the need to explore, the need to tangle with the cultural dragons be retained without also retaining the tendency to accept the lure of forbidden fruit or use one's abilities destructively? The tendency for man to seek forbidden fruit is not just because of the nature of the fruit, but part of it is the very nature of man.

The Challenge

It is neither possible nor desirable to remove from young people that which drives them either to creativity or to destruction. Not all the fruit forbidden to the young is inherently evil. Sexuality, for example, is a part of the good creation of God, yet the young are forbidden sexual intercourse. It is not because sex is evil, but rather because premaritial sexual experimentation tends to be destructive of personality. Neither are the young generally in a position to assume responsibility for the possible consequences of their sexual acts. Aggression, the herd instinct, the sex drive are inherent in man. But the desire to smoke pot or to take an alcoholic beverage are in the beginning not an end in itself, but a learned pattern of behavior.

James said, "A person is tempted when he is drawn away and trapped by his own evil desire; then his evil desire conceives and gives birth to sin; and sin when it is full-grown, gives birth to death." (James 1:14–15 TEV.) The implications seem to be that man should look for the source of evil not in the universe, in the culture, or in the objects of creation, but rather in his own misdirected desires. It is easy to pass responsibility to someone else or to blame it on the enticement of the object, thing, or person involved. We must, however, assume responsibility for our own actions and recognize that although temptations will come, we are to overcome them by the grace of God.

The present era is an exciting time in which to be alive. How can we channel the energies of youth in working for the fruit of the spirit rather than for forbidden fruit? Paul said, "The spirit produces love, joy, peace, patience, goodness, faithfulness, humility, and self-control" (Gal. 5:22, TEV). The basic idealism of youth is closely related to the fruit of the spirit; however, it is cut off from its rootage in the Judeo-Christian tradition.

I am intrigued by youth's zest for life, by the youthful desire to live every moment as if there were no promise of tomorrow. There isn't. But in their zest for life they at times do some rather stupid things. Don't we all? How does one differentiate between what is a valid celebration of life and what is pure hedonistic philosophy? An uncritical acceptance of what goes under the term of a new morality, which seems on the surface to say that anything goes as long as it is done lovingly, can lead to great difficulty. By mistaking sexual attraction, affection, or some sort of emotion for love, just about any action can be made to seem

---

KINNELON, N. J. (AP)—Despite warnings, many parents in this well-to-do community and others in the northern New Jersey hills didn't realize their children had a drug problem. Now they know.

In raids over the past few days in the posh Smoke Rise section here, 28 young people, many of them teen-agers, were arrested on various drug charges, including sale and possession of marijuana, LSD, and methedrine (speed).

The raids were sparked by the undercover work of two babyfaced policemen who posed as "rich-hippies" to infiltrate the young set, called by police "kids from good homes with good parents." But officials say the parents didn't realize the magnitude of the problem until it hit home in the raids. (Associated Press, January 21, 1970.)

---

moral. Such a view must be rejected. Acts have consequences, and one cannot ignore his neighbor when insisting on his right to do his own thing. Just as an adult style of life which worships codes of law rather than a living God must be rejected, so must the youth style of life which worships relativism or a modern hedonism rather than God.

Let us be clear about one thing. Life we can accept. It is filled with worthy challenges. The problems of the cities, slums, crime, air and water pollution, racial injustice, overpopulation, and war are enough to call forth every ounce of energy we have.

Who needs more than these to turn him on? Or could it be that these are so discouraging that people turn on to escape the reality of the world?

The nature of the influence of biological inheritance upon the formation of personality is not determining, but limiting. Social environment is a necessary, but not sufficient, explanation for the behavior of an individual. Basically, human behavior is learned and is oriented toward some satisfaction or pseudo-satisfaction. Many factors must be considered in understanding the foolhardy, "I'll try anything once." These include rebellion, the

RALEIGH (AP)—The North Carolina Highway Patrol is finding more and more drivers under the influence of non-narcotic drugs such as the barbiturates and amphetamines, Col. E. C. Guy, Patrol commander, said today.

And since the law covers only persons driving under the influence of liquor or narcotic drugs, there is nothing patrolmen can do about it unless they can charge the person with some other offenses such as speeding or drunken driving. (Associated Press, March 13, 1970.)

desire for adventure, and the availability and desirability of forbidden fruit. The desire for adventure which is so essential to cultural development cannot be retained without expecting some rebellion against the old patterns of life. Warning of the dangers inherent in such actions must be continually made. Positively, youth need to be stimulated and challenged to use their energies in solving the problems of the world. The generation gap is not so wide that it cannot be bridged by love.

2

CHEMICAL COMFORTS: PSYCHOACTIVE DRUGS

(By William S. Garmon)

The mythical age described by Aldous Huxley when he wrote *Brave New World* in 1932 has become something of a reality. The people of the United States are heavily oriented toward chemical comforts. These range all the way from mild stimulants such as caffeine and nicotine to strong depressants such as morphine or heroin. Huxley wrote:

"There was a thing called Heaven: but all the same they used to drink enormous quantities of alcohol. . . .

"There was a thing called the soul and a thing called immortality. . . .

"But they used to take morphia and cocaine. . . .

"Two thousand pharmacologists and biochemists were subsidized in A. F. 178. . . .

"Six years later it was being produced commercially. The perfect drug. . . .

"Euphoric, narcotic, pleasantly hallucinant. . . .

"All of the advantages of Christianity and alcohol; none of their defects. . . .

"Take a holiday from reality whenever you like, and come back without so much as a headache or a mythology." [1]

Whatever the problem, we are convinced that the scientists will in time produce a pill or a liquid which will either remove, prevent, or mask the problem so that it no longer pains us.

We are a nation of pill-takers. The average child becomes well acquainted with a pediatrician long before he can walk or talk. He is introduced to nice, beautiful, usually pleasant-tasting medicines which can make one well from whatever it is that causes the pain. Then, don't mother and father take all kinds of pills—white ones, red ones, blue ones, green ones, spotted ones, all the colors of the rainbow? Isn't this fun? Of course there is also the ubiquitous television set with its beautiful commercials. Well, some of them aren't really beautiful, but your attention is held. It is amazing how rapidly those little pain-killers rush through the blood system to the top of your head to rid you of all that pain.

A child learns quite early, the television set is a built-in baby-sitter, that some pills are better than others, or at least

---

DANVILLE (AP)—A 17 year-old Danville youth was convicted of marijuana possession yesterday in Danville Corporation Court and sentenced to 20 years, with 12 years suspended, and a $100 fine. (Associated Press, January 14, 1970.)

---

they get the job done more quickly. Let's see, is it the one which has a coating of something that gets there first or is it the plain one with nothing but pure pain-killer? It is difficult to remember. Which pill is it that absorbs all of that mean acid in the stomach? What do I take to go to sleep and awake looking as if

I had just left the beauty parlor? Now which pill is it that makes me less nervous, that insures a promotion, or election to the presidency of my club? Or is that a deodorant? Life gets so complicated.

In the Service of Man

Since ancient times the medical profession has used drugs in alleviating pain and in the treatment of illness. The quality of life in our world has been improved without question through the proper application of drugs. The discovery of a new drug which proves effective in the treatment or prevention of one or more of the physical or psychological ills of men brings accolades and wealth to the discoverer, or maybe it's to the company which manufactures it. One of the major contributions to increasing longevity in the United States, and in most of the world, is the ever-increasing number of drugs which have found their place in the physician's arsenal.

Drugs can be defined as chemicals used in the practice of medicine to act upon the body's own chemistry. This may be a substitute for the chemicals the body lacks, to speed up or slow down the activity of glands, organs, or to fight a specific infection which has invaded the body. More specifically the chemicals under discussion in this chapter are not all used in the practice of medicine but are those chemicals employed to speed up or to slow down the action of the central nervous system. The phrase "chemical comforts" is a meaningful one.

Come, Doctor, what pill can you give me today? Sure, my ailment may be psychosomatic or whatever you call it, but you do have some medicine for it, don't you? Is "better living through chemistry" such a bad slogan? Surely you are not going to insist that I live in the real world when there are so many beautiful ways of modifying it?

Any reading of the history of ancient cultures will acquaint one with the fact that the use of herbs, juices, barks or other natural substances in the treatment of illness is as old as man. About 5,000 years ago Chinese physicians prescribed marijuana to induce euphoria and to reduce pain. Today, however, this drug does not have a legitimate use in medicine. Alcohol has a long history of use in medicine, although much of it was self-

---

PHILADELPHIA (AP)—Narcotics violations are up more than 300 per cent here in four years and the offenders are mostly white middle-class, police say.

"Part of this picture is that the more affluent people are turning to crime," Police Commissioner Frank L. Rizzo said Sunday.

"Once the use of hard drugs was primarily the problem of poor people, black and white. Now the cost is increasing and narcotics are not so easy to get as a few years ago," Rizzo said. (Associated Press, March 16, 1970.)

---

prescribed. At present, anything which might be accomplished by alcohol as a medicine can be done as effectively, or more so, by other substances. The use of marijuana and alcohol today is not for medicinal reasons.

The opiate drugs was known to the Egyptians as early as 1500 B.C. Narcotic drugs such as morphine, paregoric, and codeine are widely used. Heroin, which is a synthetic opium-based drug, has been available since 1898, but it is not used by physicians in this country because of its highly addictive qualities. Morphine is used in alleviating pain until the cause can be located by the physicians and corrected if possible. Paregoric is used in treating some intestinal difficulties, and codeine is a common ingredient in cough syrup.

The barbiturates, tranquilizers, and amphetamines are more recent in development and have a wide range of use in the treatment of physical and mental ills. The barbiturates are widely used in the treatment of epilepsy, insomnia, and emotional and mental ills. The tranquilizers have proved to be most effective in the treatment of certain types of anxieties, tensions, emotional and mental illnesses. Many patients are able to live at home and cope with life rather than vegetate in an institution because of these drugs. The amphetamines are utilized for certain types of mild depression and as a short-term aid in weight management. Quite often these drugs are given in combination offering a wider range of treatment possibilities. Who among us has not at one time or another in recent years been treated with one of these drugs and received benefit from it? Increasingly, however, we are disturbed by the number of people who are abusing these chemicals.

Abuse of Drugs

Technically speaking, not all of the substances which are abused can be classified as drugs. Some of them are common items found around the house. A recent death caused by sniffing the contents of an aerosol can brought action by the city council of a southside Virginia city. The approved ordinance read, in part, "It shall be unlawful for any person while on public property, including, but not limited to, public schools and grounds, parks, streets and public thoroughfares to inhale the gases or vapors from glue, household or model cements, gasoline, paint thinner, lighter fluid, nail polish remover or other products producing a vapor composed of either toluene, acetone or isopropanol either directly or through pre-packaged aerosols containing freon." One is immediately made to wonder why the ordinance was limited to acts committed on public property, but nevertheless the forbidden acts range across most of the non-drug items used in so-called drug experimentation by youngsters.

Modern man has at his disposal an ever-increasing number of ways to satisfy his desire to run away from the real world, to escape from all pain and discomfort. He can experience ease, comfort, pleasure, and even euphoria with the aid of chemicals. Unfortunately one has to raise the question as to whether or not man can be man and live in a drug-modified reality? Rest assured, however, that if something can be abused man will find a way to do it. For probably five thousand years some men have

---

NEW YORK (AP)—The son of a top Chicago bank executive, seized Sunday after a high-speed auto chase down Fifth Avenue, was ordered held in $100,000 bail yesterday for his involvement in an international dope smuggling gang. (Associated Press, January 27, 1970.)

---

abused chemical comforts. Drug abuse is not just a modern phenomenon. In the case of some drugs, it may not be as extensive in degree as in some earlier periods in history, but modern man has a wider selection of substances to abuse, and in a highly technological age the effects of abuse have more ramifications.

When drug abuse comes into the average conversation, most minds turn to the drug-crazed heroin addict, to young people with long hair who are dirty, ragged, drop-outs from society, or to college students who are experimenting with LSD, marijuana or some other chemical. There are really few limits to the possibilities for experimentations. However, drug abuse is not limited to young people. It is difficult to know how many people are misusing drugs, legitimate ones.

Drug abusers fall into many categories. Some people use drugs for specific purposes such as the student who uses amphetamines to keep awake in preparing for exams or the housewife who needs a pick-up to get through the household tasks. Such individuals may or may not exhibit dependence upon drugs. Another group uses drugs for kicks or goes on an occasional spree not far different from the old beer bust. While this group may develop some psychological dependence, physical dependence will be rare because of the sporadic nature of usage. The third type of drug abuser is the hard-core addict. These persons exhibit strong psychological and at times physical dependence upon drugs, depending on the drug being used.

Drug-dependence, which is the preferred term now being used in the literature to replace the words "habituating" and "addicting," can be physical dependency, psychological dependency, or a combination of these. Abuse of the substances such as alcohol or the narcotic drugs can produce both physical and psychological dependency. There is some debate about whether or not the sedative, hypnotic, and depressant drugs produce only psychological or both psychological and physical

HOUSTON, Tex. (AP)—More than 100 policemen arrested 114 persons Friday night and early yesterday in narcotics raids that included searches of taverns, lounges, pool halls and private homes.

Police had 95 indictments naming 58 alleged narcotics peddlers. The raids reportedly netted 27 of those indicted.

Most of those sought were charged with selling heroin, marijuana or LSD to agents posing as junkies or pushers. (Associated Press, January 25, 1970.)

dependence. LSD and marijuana are generally considered to produce only psychological dependency, which can be extremely harmful in itself. Abusers of drugs classed as narcotics, stimulants, and sedatives, as well as some of the tranquilizers, are said to build tolerance; that is, an increasing amount of the drug is needed to produce the effect desired. Once dependency has developed, withdrawal can be painful and dangerous. Withdrawal from the barbiturates may be more difficult than from heroin. Anyone hung-up on drugs should consult with a physician before attempting withdrawal. While not absolutely necessary, it would be a wise precaution.

Millions of persons in the United States use prescription barbiturates, tranquilizers, or stimulants such as the amphetamines each year. There is no way of documenting the number of persons who abuse these drugs. Some estimate that there are as many as 20 million drug abusers in the country. Such a figure cannot, however, be accepted as fact. There is no doubt that many college students abuse amphetamines. So many long-distance truck drivers use pep pills to remain awake while on long runs that the term "co-pilots" is a slang term identification. It is an open secret that many professional sports figures are immune to pain while on the playing field. Many professional persons caught in the stress-strain of trying to "make it" take a barbiturate in the evening to sleep and an amphetamine in the morning to get going again. Housewives interested in keeping a trim figure are often known to stockpile diet-pill prescriptions, from several physicians, in order to obtain a large number of pills. These often find their way to white-collar pill parties. Pills and marijuana are now replacing alcohol in some circles as the accepted way for a genial host to entertain. Pot parties are not limited to the college scene.

AMARILLO, Tex. (AP)—A young mother who worked as an undercover narcotics agent at a high school says her most frightening moment came when a young man said he had slipped an LSD cube in her soft drink. . . .

The climax came last week when authorities, armed with grand jury indictments, arrested a large number of alleged drug offenders.

It was four months of pot parties and deception and lonely hours of ferreting out drug contacts, she said in an interview, permitted by the court on condition that she not discuss certain points. (Associated Press, January 25, 1970.)

Without doubt some physicians are too quick to write a prescription—some from humanitarian concern, others simply to get a hypochondriac off their backs. Most of the abuse probably comes not from drugs obtained legally, although there is undoubtedly some of this. It is estimated that nearly half of the amphetamines and barbiturates manufactured each year find their way into illegal markets. Some drugs are produced by unethical companies where quality control is of no concern—only the fast buck. In other words these are bootleg outfits.

Alcohol remains the chief drug abused in the United States. Over two-thirds of our population fifteen years of age or over drink alcoholic beverages to some extent. The number of alcoholics, addictive or compulsive drinkers, is variously estimated at between five and seven million. An increasing number of young people are experimenting with marijuana and other drugs. It can be safely estimated that over one-half of the population uses, and many abuse, one or more forms of chemical comforts each day. While some are happy to consume limited amounts of alcohol, tobacco, caffeine (oh, yes, these too are chemical comforts), or some drug normally used in medical treatment, others lose control of their appetites and become dependent upon drugs.

Some chemical substances are more highly addictive or habit-forming than others, but the substance involved is always just one factor. The personality, and at times the biochemistry, of the individual makes a tremendous difference. The cultural and social attitude toward drug use and the immediate social context in the case of the experimenter can be a factor. Most young people do not get started on drugs because of a pusher, but from the pressure of the peer group. Even the experience one has from psychoactive drugs is often determined in part by what the group expects, not actually by what the chemical does.

The depressing action of alcohol, sedatives, tranquilizers, or narcotics operate to relieve for a time the discomforts of anxiety, pain, or frustration to which the flesh is heir. Stimulants such as one of the amphetamines can temporarily remove the feelings of depression. Psychoactive drugs change the moods of the users. One could almost believe that soon there will be such an array of mood pills that one will be able to alter his mood to fit the circumstances.

Abuse of Stimulants and Depressives

Drug abuse has become so widespread that it has been neces-

BOSTON (AP)—Drinking in the home contributes more to harmful accidents than had been thought previously, a year-long study of 8,000 emergency-ward patients showed. . . .

Of those injured in the home 22 per cent had been drinking, judging from indications of alcohol detected by the breathalyzer test.

Of those injured in fights or assaults 56 per cent had been drinking. (Associated Press, October 12, 1969.)

---

sary to place the dispensing of many drugs under strict legal controls. Narcotics have long been controlled. Since 1966 a large number of depressants, stimulants, and hallucinogens have been placed under control. This was made necessary by obvious drug abuse. People who abuse marijuana, hallucinogens, stimulants, or depressants rarely come to the attention of the authorities unless they are arrested for being involved in some criminal act. Even so, some authorities are convinced that the abuse of barbiturates and amphetamines is a greater problem than the use of heroin and marijuana. It is the use of the latter which frightens most people. Since subsequent chapters in this book are devoted to marijuana and heroin use, a more definite note should be made at this point about the abuse of barbiturates and amphetamines.

Barbiturates are known by many slang terms such as "barbs," "candy," "goofballs," "sleeping pills," or given labels according to the specific shape or color of the commercial product. One red and blue capsule of amobarbital sodium combined with secobarbital sodium is known as "rainbows," "reds and blues," and "double trouble."

Physical dependence on barbiturates does not develop under normal dosage used in medical practice; however, it can and does occur when used excessively. Tolerance develops, that is, and increasing dosage is needed to produce the effect desired. Withdrawal is exceedingly dangerous and can cause death. Convulsions and hallucinations are common. Barbiturates are the second most commonly used agent for suicide; however, some of these are accidental in that the victim was in a confused state of mind from the effects of the drug and took more than he realized. Another common accident which produces suicide is to combine alcohol and a barbiturate. Since both are depressants, it is possible to consume a lethal dosage without being aware of the danger.

Abuse of barbiturates is marked by sluffing of speech, staggering, loss of balance and falling, quick temper, and a tendency to excessive quarrelsomeness. Usually the appearance of drunkenness without indications of the use of alcohol points to barbiturate usage.

Amphetamines stimulate the central nervous system. They are known as "pep pills," "co-pilots," "bennies," "eye openers," among other terms, or by names related to the shape or color of the capsules and tablets. Amphetamine sulfate in rose-colored, heart-shaped tablets is called "roses," "hearts," or "bennies." Dextroamphetamine sulfate in an orange-colored, heart-shaped tablet is known, among other terms, as "dexies" after a trade name of the drug.

Abuse of amphetamines produces excitation, alertness, increased initiative and activity, and the ability to go without sleep for protracted periods of time. Since the body develops tolerance to the drug, the abuser increases his dosage gradually, which wildly exaggerates the normal effects of the drug. He becomes talkative, restless, shaky, has trouble sleeping, and perspires profusely. The pupils of the eyes will be enlarged. In serious cases a drug-induced psychosis will develop which will resemble schizophrenia, with delusions and hallucinations both auditory and visual. The individual may think, for example, that he is covered with insects or may see insects and angels coming out of the woodwork.

Amphetamines do not cause physical addiction, but psychological or emotional dependence on the drugs can develop. Perhaps the most dangerous, but not necessarily the most abused, drug in the class is methamphetamine. This is the drug which is chemically related to amphetamine, but produces more central nervous system activity and less effect on blood pressure and pulse rate than amphetamine. The abuse of methamphetamine, or "Speed," "Crystal," and "Meth" as the drug is known in slang terminology, is thought to be widespread. When it is injected in large doses the user experiences something akin to sexual orgasm. As was soon discovered by the hippie drug cult, "Speed kills." This is not just a play on words, for users often build to more than one hundred times the normal medic

NEWARK, Calif. (AP)—Susan Dusio, 13, is bad news to local drug pushers.

The 4-foot-7, 70 pound eight grader at MacGregor Junior High School is almost entirely responsible for arranging a week of drug-abuse education that taught 640 teen-agers what the drug scene is all about. (Associated Press, March 19, 1970.)

inal dose which may be repeated several times a day. It should not be a surprise that such users are often found in an acute toxic state with death as a possible outcome. Irritability, confusion, delirium, assaultiveness, and hallucinations mark the behavior of the abuser. Depression and fatigue appear in the user if he has not come to a violent end before the effects of the drug are over.

Why Chemical Comforts?

The present generation lives in a pleasure-loving age, but whether this is more marked than in all other periods of history is debatable. Undoubtedly more people now have an opportunity to participate in the good things of life than has ever been true at any point in the history of time. They are constantly being urged from every side to enjoy ease, pleasure, and comfort. Pleasure is currently one of the chief values of our society. How far should one go in self-indulgence? How far must the Christian go in self-denial? Does Christianity reject all human pleasure whether of the mind or of the body? Hardly, but where is the line to be drawn? There was a time in the Calvinistic branch of Protestantism when almost anything which gave pleasure was viewed with suspicion, if not labeled an outright sin. It is now accepted in most circles that man should celebrate life. Have the modern descendants of Calvin gone too far in accepting chemical comforts? Perhaps the more pressing question is, Can man live in the modern world with all of its stresses and strains without some of the chemical comforts which enable him to cope with life by modifying reality at times?

Not all drugs are abused. If they are used under the care of a physician, in moderation, and for socially approved reasons—such as for relaxation, sleep, relief of pain, and restoration of energy lost from temporary physical disability—few persons will raise an ethical question. Only a minority of Americans raise questions about the moderate use of alcohol. Many young people do not see any problem with the moderate use of marijuana. They are honest in this. However, when any chemical

---

WASHINGTON (AP)—The Senate heard yesterday a strong challenge to the constitutionality of no-warning narcotics raids as it debated an administration bill to curb illegal drug traffic.

"This section permits narcotics agents to act like burglars and enter a house by stealth or by force," said Sen. Sam J. Ervin, Jr., D–N. C. (Associated Press, January 25, 1970.)

---

substance is used for such purposes as to increase sociability, for kicks, to rebel, to escape from reality, or when social consequences can be tragic, serious questions must be raised. Let us keep things in proper perspective. Probably more Americans abuse food than any other substance taken into the body. The basic causes for overeating are probably some of the same factors which make one vulnerable to excessive use of chemical comforts. Over-eating is excused far more often than the other self-indulgences of men. Maybe this is as it should be, for the social consequences are not usually as great, at least in the short run.

Excessive use of alcohol creates more problems with tragic consequences than the use of all other chemical comforts in current use combined. The use of alcohol is, however, part of the warp and woof of American culture and it will take generations to change the pattern, if indeed it can be changed. One of the major reasons for so much use of alcohol is the desire for sociability. The same thing is true of the use of marijuana among young people, yet few adults can see the relationship. In public discussions when this issue is considered, few adults, if any, are willing to examine the matter. They are too much interested in what the young people are doing wrong. This is said not just in defense of the young, but in an effort to see it like it is. One must raise a question about the head-in-the-sand attitude of most people about the alcohol problem. The evil effects of alcohol abuse are well documented, and there is no need to reproduce them here. However, let us take one example. Americans of different persuasions about the Vietnam War are genuinely distressed that the number of young American's killed in this conflict is approaching the 40,000 mark. Massive protests have been mounted against what many consider a waste of young manhood. The rightness or wrongness of our involvement in Vietnam should continue to be debated, but can anyone dare debate the rightness of 25,000 Americans being killed and other thousands injured or disabled permanently each year because some automobile drivers insist upon driving and drinking? Should not massive protest be mounted? Talk about senseless waste!

While we are on the subject of driving, a person intoxicated on marijuana shouldn't be behind the wheel either, nor a person loaded with barbiturates.

Much drug experimentation by young people is done in a group and in part to gain group acceptance. Loneliness, despair, and hopelessness can lead to drug-experimentation. Some of this is searching after meaning in existence, some of it is an attempt to escape reality. For whatever cause, the drug scene is disturbing. It is a social problem of major concern.

Can guidelines be developed which will assist Christians in evaluating current practices of drug use? Perhaps it should be recognized that the value system of any society is always changing and that the church gets caught in the middle sometimes. The old middle-class value of deferred gratification which has been supported by the Christian doctrine of self-denial has largely disappeared. Being oppressed during life in this world was once believed by some to be almost a sure sign that there would be a better life in the world to come for such a person. This is no longer accepted as valid. Current emphasis is upon the fact that God intended man to subdue the world, to enjoy it. It does not follow that man must be completely adjusted to the world around him. It is out of anxiety that both creative and destructive forces arise.

Another fact must be faced realistically. It may be that man cannot live in the present world without the temporary or occasional aid of chemical comforts. It is scarcely Christian to

MARSEILLE, France (AP)—The lab looked like a filthy laundry room: dryers, long tables, stoves and the kind of pots used for boiling diapers. Jammed into a corner were a dozen clear plastic bags stuffed with a white substance that could have been soap powder. . . .

The room in a villa called La Roserai in the hills back of Marseille was the heroin-making laboratory of Joseph Cesari, a bartender and seaman who had become France's biggest narcotics chemist. . . . He went to jail for seven years in 1965.

About 80 per cent of the drug traffic entering American ports from Europe is thought to come from here.

Marseille heroin, distilled from morphine base received from Turkey and the Middle East, runs 80 to 90 per cent pure. Addicts in the United States are said to prefer its whiteness to Mexican heroin, a kind of beige in color and only 50–60 per cent without imperfection. . . . (Associated Press, November 4, 1969.)

---

drive man to self-destruction, but neither is it Christian to so satiate him with chemical comforts that he finds a savior in a pill, a liquid or a gas. Man stands under the constant tension between his Christian faith and the social practices of his daily life. All stand under the judgment of God. It is only in judgment that forgiveness and restoration of fellowship between man and God and among men can be a reality.

For whatever reasons, human beings have long been willing to experiment with ingesting, chewing, eating, drinking, smoking, sniffing, or injecting in some form a wide variety of substances. This desire to eat, drink, smoke, or use drugs may be dangerous or safe depending upon the nature and the amount of the substance involved and the reasons behind the usage.

Whereas the physician uses drugs in an effort to obtain normality in the body, the drug abuser is usually after more marked results—deep sedation on the one hand or euphoria on the other. The use of chemical comforts does not automatically lead to drug abuse, but that large numbers of persons are abusing them can scarcely be questioned.

NOTES

1. Aldous Huxley, *Brave New World* (New York: The Modern Library, 1946), pp. 62–63.

3

"ACAPULCO GOLD"

(By Phil Strickland)

It was the mid-1960's when the rush really began. Suddenly, a "gold" rush that would touch the lives of a large segment of our society was on. This time, a new kind of gold was creating the excitement. "Acapulco Gold" (marijuana), along with a myriad of other drugs, had suddenly caught the imagination of significant numbers of American youth. The young generation, seemingly capitulating to the incessant bombardment of drug stimuli, had turned to the "panacea pills" their parents had been using for years. But, youth being youth, it was necessary to do their own thing, not their parent's. Thoroughly addicted to the "magic potion notion," they went in search of their own reality eraser. LSD was the first experiment, but it did not take long for bright, educated young people to generally reject something as dangerous as "acid."

One drug, however, began to receive widespread support. As the support increased, so did the use, until it became obvious that "Mary Jane" had entered the lives of a vast number of our young people. But this created a problem. "Mary Jane" was illegal, and as the use increased, so did the risk of spending a substantial part of life behind bars because of a felony conviction. Thus, there arose the demand for legalization. With the call for legalization came the reaction against it, until marijuana

became the focal point, the symbol of the rebellion and alienation that many young people feel.

That it became such a symbol is hardly surprising. There
were, first, the excessive drug laws that declared that smoking
pot was as bad as about anything one could do except commit
treason or first degree murder. Such laws were, and are, vulnerable. There was, in addition, the fact that pot was also the safest
drug around that would cause an up-tight reaction by adults.
Interestingly, young people discovered that they could blow
their minds by using alcohol, and Mom and Dad, sipping their
cocktails, would mildly admonish them. "It's all a part of growing up." But, let them get wind of a few puffs of pot and they
would go screaming around the room. What a neat way to rebel!

Because of the symbolism, it has become extremely difficult
for both sides of the generation gap to view marijuana with any
sense of objectivity. Both young and old seem to possess an
amazing accumulation of answers and an astonishing absence of
facts. As the debate has grown in intensity, it has been increasingly characterized by generalizations, exaggerations, misrepre-
sentations and massive confusion.

It is important to begin to clear out the underbrush and
distortions in order to see the picture as it really is. For an
understanding of the drug is necessary before there can be any
determination of what to do with it. Two basic questions must
be considered. First, what is "Acapulco Gold?" Second, what
does it do?

There is, however, a preliminary question that deserves attention. To what extent is the use of marijuana a real problem? Is
marijuana, in fact, more symbol than reality? Has the mass
media so distorted a few instances of use that the impression of

NEW YORK (AP)—Ralph de Jesus is a heroin addict who says he started using drugs a year ago. He is 12. "I used to see my friend doing it and I didn't want to be left out," he said.

widespread use is a fiction created by the image makers?

There is little doubt that vast numbers of young people have actually used marijuana at one time or another. However, as with any illegal activity, it is extremely difficult to get a clear picture of the amount of activity. Estimates are tremendously varied, and all of them must be taken with a whole shaker of salt.

Dr. Leo Hollister, for example, has commented that pot has become so entrenched in our society that we have passed the point of no return. We must, then, decide how to live with it. Other evaluations are less spectacular.

A number of well-publicized estimates have been made. In 1968, it was estimated that 60 to 70 percent of college students used marijuana. A Gallup Poll of the same year, however, suggested that only about six percent of college students had actually tried marijuana. It should be noted that nearly all student estimates tend to run rather high, possibly out of a sub-conscious attempt at justification by peer acceptance.

In 1969, another Gallup Poll indicated that 12 out of every 100 young adults in their 20's said that they had tried marijuana. When projected to the total population, this meant that some five million young adults were experimenters or users.

The poll also estimated that a total of ten million Americans had tried pot and another five million would try a marijuana cigarette if it were offered to them.

Later estimates tend to make one suspect that the five million must have had cigarettes offered to them. Joel Fort, who has written extensively on drugs, now suspects that there are between 12 and 20 million regular users. And Dr. Stanley Yolles, director of the National Institute of Mental Health, recently estimated in testimony before a House subcommittee that from eight to 12 million people have tried marijuana, and perhaps the figure would run as high as 20 million.

Obviously, no one is very sure how much marijuana is being used. There is, however, general agreement concerning a couple of trends. First, it is apparent that experimentation with pot is still increasing. At one college, a study indicated that those who had some experience with marijuana was 21% in 1967, 57% in 1968, and the projection for 1969 was 70%. Such figures may be above the norm, but they illustrate the trend toward increasing experimentation.

It is also obvious that drug use is sifting into the younger grades. "If it is all right for big brother, it is good enough for me." As marijuana is accepted among older groups, it becomes enticing to the younger child who is in a hurry to grow up and do everything the big kids are doing. Dr. Thomas Ungerleider, who works with drug problems in Los Angeles, has observed that in 1965, the average subject of their studies was 21 years old. Now the average age is down to 14 or 15. A number of drug games are becoming increasingly popular with the very young. For example, "fruit cocktail" is a game played at parties. Everyone snitches a few of the pills that parents have around the house. At the party, the pills are dumped into a common sack. The sack is shaken up, then passed around the room with each youngster taking a pill as it goes by until they are all gone.

GAINESVILLE, Fla. (AP)—Andy Anderson wrote a poem about his drug experiences saying, "My mind is no longer my friend. It won't leave me alone."

Then he burned himself to death.

County Judge John L. Connell made public Tuesday the poem and a note in which Anderson wrote: "The drug experience has filled me with fear and doubts of myself. I cannot go on. Please try to remember my good points and excuse this final act of desperation."

There is, then, little doubt that we are talking about a problem that is significant and growing. Thus, it becomes important to understand the virtues and sins of Mary Jane. If it is, in fact, harmless both to persons and to society, then there is little to be concerned about. If, on the other hand, marijuana tends to be destructive to both individuals and society, then a response to its use which is appropriate and effective must be determined quickly.

What Is "Acapulco Gold?"

Marijuana is a preparation which is produced from the plant, *cannabis sativa L.* The plant has long, slender, sawtooth edged leaves. It is a healthy plant, easily grown in temperate climates throughout the world. Men have known of its existence for centuries and have used it both as a mind influencing drug and as a source of rope and paper products. Mention is made of the drug as a mind-affector as far back as an ancient Chinese manuscript dated around 3,000 B.C. Later manuscripts, from around 1200 B.C., mention the plant as a source of fibers for rope.

There are many varieties of the plant. Differences in these are caused by soil, sunlight, water and cultivation. The plant is easily grown in the United States. Although it is illegal, many acres are discovered each year and thousands more are never located by the authorities. It is frequently discovered on remote public land where its discovery does not automatically relate it to the owner of the property. Recently, enterprising students have delighted in expressing their rebellion by planting pot in public places. It has been found growing along turnpikes, in city parks, on campuses, and on state capital grounds.

The different varieties of marijuana may have varying potency, but the main factor that determines the strength of a dosage is the different parts of the plant. Men have experimented for centuries with the varying effects of stalk, seeds, leaves, flowers, and resins. Marijuana generally refers to a preparation made from any of those parts of the female plant, except the stalk.

Some parts of the plant, then, are more potent than others. The primary factor that determines this difference is the amount of the active ingredient, tetrahydrocannabinol, that is present in a particular part of the plant. (There is some argument regarding whether this is the only active ingredient. It seems obvious, however, that it accounts for the major amount of activity.) The difference is well illustrated by three *cannibas* preparations that have existed for years in India. *Bhanq, ganja* and *charas* are all produced from the same basic plant. *Bhang,* the weakest, is produced from whole male and female plants mixed together. *Ganja* is made from the tops of female plants and is three to four times as strong as *bhang. Charas,* the most powerful, is made from the resin produced by the flowers. It is three to four times as powerful as *Ganja. Bhang,* the weakest, is the nearest to being comparable to American marijuana.

The pot used in America is very weak. It usually begins on some farm in Mexico. The marijuana, both male and female plants, are mowed. Usually the mowing occurs when the foliage is the thickest to give the most weight. This is not the time of greatest potency. The plants are then pressed into "bricks." Molasses is often added to make the marijuana stick together and to add weight. It is not uncommon for a "brick" to also include sugar and a few sticks and stones. When one recalls that only a few parts of the female plant are really potent, he realizes that the brick one gets in the United States is of quite low potency.

THC, tetrahydrocannabinol, was first isolated in 1940, but it was not until 1967 that science learned to chemically produce it. Working in the laboratories of Jerusalem's Hebrew University with a grant from our National Institute of Mental Health, thirty-seven-year-old Rafael Mechoulam made "Acapulco Gold" in a test tube. His discovery has been closely guarded to prevent the underworld from discovering the process. Only a few researchers have been allowed to use the formula for additional research.

Frequently, the word gets out that pure THC is available on the black market. Pushers come across with a new pill which is supposedly "loaded with the pure stuff." To date, they have been loaded with everything but THC. There has never yet been a THC pill identified on the black market. The chemistry is extremely complex, and there is little possibility that it will be available to pushers for some time to come.

Is Marijuana a Narcotic?

A great deal of confusion has arisen over whether or not marijuana is a narcotic. A small Texas newspaper, describing a raid that had taken place, reported that "the police found a considerable amount of narcotics, the main one being marijuana." Such reporting, unfortunately, has been far too frequent, for it has led people to associate marijuana with the hard narcotics such as heroin and morphine. This misunderstanding has been perpetuated by the fact that for years marijuana was under the jurisdiction of the Bureau of Narcotics. The agents were referred to as "narcotic agents." In 1968, the Federal Bureau of Narcotics of the Treasury Department and the Bureau of Drug Abuse Control of the Food and Drug Administration were combined to form the Bureau of Narcotics and Dangerous Drugs in the Department of Justice. The agents, however, are still referred to as "narcs" by the press and public, furthering the image that agents are dealing with narcotic users, even if marijuana is the only drug involved.

It is true that marijuana has some narcotic-like effects, such as producing a stupor or depressing reaction. But the main characteristics of the drug are hallucinogenic, and there is general consensus in the medical community today that the proper classification is that of a mild hallucinogen. What is it usually called?

Is grass kin to *cannabis?* If one is talking to his local gardener, the relationship between grass and *cannabis* may be rather distant. However, if the conversation is with a member of the contemporary drug culture, one discovers that grass and *cannabis* are identical. The drug culture has precipitated a vocabulary all its own. Marijuana is a good example. "Acapulco Gold," weed, pot, grass, hay, "boo," tea, and "Mary Jane" are all references of marijuana. Hash, or hashish, is a reference to a more powerful preparation produced from the resin of the plant. It is generally thought of as a Middle East preparation, though it can be, and often is, made from any *cannabis* plant.

Where Does It Come from?

The pot market in the United States has grown astronomically in the last few years. As the demand has skyrocketed, there has been a rush to supply the quantities desired.

Most of the marijuana used in America is grown and imported from Mexico. It is generally estimated that in excess of 275 tons of marijuana is annually smuggled into the United States. This means that the weekly intake is about five tons, or nearly one-half ton a day. The vast majority of this comes from Mexico. Enforcement agents are able to detect and seize only about two tons a year, or about two percent of the total.

The massive movement of marijuana through our young society is a testimony to our affluence. The farmer in Mexico will get about $3.25 a pound, or about $7.00 a kilo. The United

States dealer, then, will get up to $200 a pound, depending on the location and the market at the moment.

It is ironical that there has been some public criticism of the Mexican government for failing to control the growth of marijuana. It must be remembered that the Mexican government would not have the problem if it were not for the tremendous demand that originates in the United States. Even so, their government has put extensive efforts into locating and destroying the plant.

How Is It Used?

There are a number of ways to get "high" on marijuana. By far the most popular of these is smoking it in hand-rolled cigarettes referred to as joints, sticks, or reefers. To "blow a stick" means to puff a joint. The way in which a cigarette is smoked is important. It is possible, if the cigarette is smoked with shallow breathing, to feel no effect at all. The more experienced smoker will inhale and hold the smoke. The last inch or so of the cigarette, referred to as the "roach" or "snipe," is particularly potent.

Marijuana may also be eaten, drunk, or smoked in pipes. Generally, it is eaten with cookies or sweets. It may be drunk mixed with soft drinks or alcoholic drinks, but is usually made into a tea. Marijuana cookbooks are available, and some young couples keep it on the table with the salt and pepper shakers to "season" food.

How Does One Detect a User?

It is extremely difficult to detect the casual use of marijuana. Indeed, there is real danger in trying too hard to be aware of its use. Too often, parents get up-tight and suspicious because Johnny's eyes are a little red, when in fact Johnny has hay fever. Johnny then becomes disturbed that Mom and Dad have so little faith in him and this may be just enough to make him rebel and go smoke a weed or two.

There are practically no physical signs of use. Usually, about the only observable physiological change is an increase in the pulse rate. Sleepiness will frequently develop, but this cannot be used as a real basis of detection.

Burning marijuana does have a very distinctive smell, something like the odor of burning weeds. The expert may use this to detect use, but it is again difficult for a novice to apply.

Possibly the main phenomenon for which the parent should watch is a change in life style. The serious user's whole life will begin to orient itself around the drug. Friends may change, if former friends insist on remaining straight. Hobbies, sports, school and other important aspects of his life may decrease in importance with no new, open interests taking their places. If this happens, the parent may have genuine cause for concern.

What Does "Acapulco Gold" Do?

The extensive marijuana debate has not centered on the basic information that has been examined thus far. Rather, the debate, while expressed in terms of legalization, has been over the question of whether or not pot is harmful to the individual or to society. At this point, the airways are jammed with a plethora of claims and counterclaims. "Smoke one of those cigarettes and you'll never have a normal kid." "It's healthy, relaxes your body." "I knew a boy that went berserk from one cigarette." "Only the straights think that anything is wrong with it." "That stuff eats up your brain." Such statements, ad infinitum, are those most heard when the subject of pot is discussed.

Why such a vast diversity of views? The primary reason probably lies in the fact that while the subject is deeply important and everyone has an opinion, the facts we have on which to base those opinions are scant, indeed. This was obvious in a trial in Massachusetts which faced the issue of whether marijuana is really harmful. Both sides were able to elicit the testimony of a whole stable of thoroughbred experts who held views directly divergent from the others.

It is impossible, therefore, to determine the real value of marijuana at this time. The assayers are still out conducting tests. There is much that we surely do not know and there is little that we surely know. There is, however, enough evidence to at least establish some presumptions, some preliminary findings that will help us with the basic question of whether pot is harmful to the individual and to society. Even in the Massachusetts trial, cross-examination established that there were a number of things on which both sides agreed.

Effects on the Individual

What is the usual reaction to smoking pot?

Suddenly, the parent discovers that little George has been smoking pot. Usually his first question, a normal one for a genuinely concerned parent, is what effect has this had on George.

By far the most common reaction is brief, mild intoxication not unlike mild alcohol intoxication. This basic reaction is influenced by several factors. Obviously, it is primarily influenced by the size of the dose of THC that is taken in. But, it is also influenced by the person himself and the environment at the time the marijuana is taken. Drs. Zinberg and Weil, the directors of the Boston double-blind study expressed the above in terms of "set" and "setting." Set, the person's expectations and personality type, and setting, the total emotional mood of the environment and the persons in it, were both found to be major factors in the way a person reacted to marijuana. The study was important, in that it was one of the first double-blind studies, which means that at the time of testing neither the user nor the tester knew whether the subject was actually smoking pot or an inactive placebo from the male plant. Other studies such as the 1939 study by the Chopras, a husband and wife team, have verified that the use of mild marijuana generally produces a mild result.

There is, however, some evidence that acute intoxication can develop from limited use. This is not surprising when one remembers that set and setting are variables as well as dosage. Another 1939 report which was recorded in the Journal of the American Medical Association, described fourteen patients who developed acute intoxication, sometimes after smoking only a single cigarette. Such things as mental confusion, hallucinations, perceptual changes, anxiety and hysterical reactions were found to accompany the intoxication. It should be noted that the report has been criticized, as has the Chopras' report, for a lack of scientific "controls."

The 1938 to 1944 study by Mayor LaGuardia's Committee

on Marijuana was the first significant research done in this country. Basically, the study emphasized the importance of dosage. Mild doses seemed to produce mild reactions and strong doses produced strong reactions which were, in a few cases, very disturbing. The study utilized electroencephalograms, behavior pattern studies and intelligence tests. No lasting mental or physical deterioration was found.

Recent studies done by Dr. Leo Hollister of California, using pure THC, show somewhat different results. Dr. Hollister has found that even relatively small doses of marijuana may have some clinical effects, such as disrupting short-term memory.

Does a Person Become Addicted to Marijuana?

Actually, the question could be better stated, for authorities generally agree that "dependence" is the preferred term. There are two possible kinds of dependence, physical and psychic (mental and emotional). When a person is physically dependent on a drug, it means that his body has developed a need for the addicting substance. When that substance is not present, the body has to make physical adjustments to live without the addicting agent. The period of adjustment, withdrawal, can be extremely painful. Generally, the narcotic, depressant drugs create physical dependence and the stimulant and hallucinogenic drugs do not. There is no evidence that marijuana causes physical dependence. Psychic dependence is a different story. There is considerable evidence that drug dependency frequently develops among pot users. The person becomes more and more psychologically dependent upon the escape provided by the "high." Often, he begins to prefer the mood resulting from the marijuana to the undrugged state.

WASHINGTON (UPI)—The government's chief research in mental health reported Wednesday that new studies have turned up "troublesome facts" about harmful side effects of marijuana.

He said the information makes it "impossible to give marijuana a clean bill of health in any discussion on the continued restriction of its use."

It has been known for years that psychic dependence can be much more devastating than physical dependence. It is relatively easy to cure a heroin addict from his physical need for the drug. There has been very little success, however, in curing his psychological dependency.

Tolerance is somewhat related at this point. Tolerance basically means that the body tends to adjust to a particular dose. So, in order to get the same effect, it becomes necessary to take larger and larger doses. This phenomenon causes many heroin addicts to periodically submit themselves to hospital care, not to be cured, but to bring their habits down to a lower level. Tolerance tends to behave erratically with the hallucinogenic drugs. There has been, for example, some evidence of a reverse tolerance with marijuana whereby lower doses cause the same reaction rather than higher doses. About the only accurate statement that can be made is that the tolerance reaction of a particular person toward marijuana cannot be predicted.

What Happens to Perception?

When asked what one thinks of first when he thinks of marijuana, the reply is frequently given by adults that they think of a person who has lost all ability to judge time and space. While the belief is often exaggerated, it does have basis in fact.

Authorities generally agree that at least minor distortion can occur with even very small doses. The phenomenon seems to be more prevelant in novice users than in experienced ones.

Dr. Stanley Yolles, in the earlier-mentioned testimony, said that pot often causes distortions resulting in dizziness or sluggishness. A number of other studies have reached the same conclusion, including the recent work of Dr. Hollister and similar research using pure THC performed at the Addiction Research Center of the U. S. Public Health Service Hospital at Lexington. Dr. Louria of New York adds his name to this list as he affirms that marijuana causes time and space distortion.

Are Mental Functions Impaired?

Here, again, there is an impressive array of authorities on both sides. The Boston studies indicated little, if any, temporary loss of reasoning ability. On the other hand, Dr. Hollister, utilizing self-reporting scales, is finding a persistent loss of ability to think clearly. Dr. Yolles agrees that marijuana interferes with the thinking process and recent memory and weakens the power to concentrate.

A general analysis of the reports leads one to the conclusion that even small doses cause some temporary decline in the ability to think clearly. As the dosage increases, so does the impairing of the mental functions. Major impairment can occur from extremely high doses. It is clear that a great deal of study still needs to be done in this area.

Do Psychotic Reactions Ever Occur?

A considerable amount of attention and controversy has centered around the question of marijuana and psychotic reactions. Many hallucinogenics cause such reactions frequently. But it has been argued that while pot is a hallucinogen, it is such a mild one that it does not usually cause psychotic behavior. The argument is sound, but the "usually" is quite important.

A number of cases of marijuana-induced psychosis have been reported in this country. Generally, these seem to have occurred among inexperienced users. Such episodes are fairly rare and seldom last more than a day or so, but this does not alleviate the fact that they do exist. There is substantial evidence that such reactions can be precipitated by even small amounts of pot. Dr. Louria observes that psychotic reactions seldom if ever result from a stable person smoking one cigarette; in unstable persons, *one* can trigger psychosis. A number of such reactions are mentioned in the findings of the 1944 LaGuardia report. Similar confirmation of mild, temporary psychoses is found in Army research released in the early part of 1970.

WASHINGTON (UPI)—A former Army sergeant who witnessed the alleged My Lai massacre told a Senate hearing today that a majority of the GIs who participated smoked marijuana. He said some of them did so the night before the accident.

A second witness, a former Army psychiatrist who worked with drug users in Vietnam, testified that if the soldiers were "chronic pot-heads" it could have contributed to their actions.

Considerable evidence also exists that on occasion acute and prolonged psychotic reactions can occur. Large doses often cause extreme effects. Dr. Harry Wilmer, of the Langley Porter Neuropsychiatric Institute in San Francisco, has documented some prolonged psychotic reactions from marijuana use, as has Dr. Louria and a number of other men.

"Flashback" is a particularly frightening experience for drug users. When this occurs, a person goes on a "high" or gets a reaction on the basis of a drug that was taken some time before, the effects of which had supposedly worn off long ago. LSD frequently causes a return to a hallucinogenic state without taking additional dosage. There are some cases and some evidence, though very limited, of flashbacks caused solely by pot.

Is There Really Brain Deterioration?

This is another area in which the emotions far exceed the evidence. Usually, the case for brain damage has utilized studies done in India and the Middle East. These have involved very heavy users of potent *cannabis* derivatives such as hashish or *charas*. A number of cases of insanity, supposedly from the *cannabis*, have been reported. The studies have been heavily criticized, however, because of the lack of adequate controls or record keeping. The fact that large numbers of Indian people in mental hospitals have smoked pot proves very little, since it is also true that the majority have come from poverty, drunk milk, and so forth.

However, at least one credible study has indicated the possibility that marijuana might affect the brain. Dr. Robert White, professor of psychiatry at the University of Texas Medical Branch at Galveston has reported abnormalities in brain patterns in cats that were injected with regular doses for at least eight to ten days. The alterations continued after the doses had been terminated. This is, of course, far from conclusive evidence, but it raises a concern which certainly needs the continued attention of the scientific community.

How Does Marijuana Influence Personality?

Thus far our concern has been what marijuana does to a person physically. But, just as important a consideration is the emotional and psychological change that may result from its use. In fact, this may eclipse the physical in its importance, for often the emotional problems are much more difficult to deal with than are the physical problems.

There is little doubt that one can find a considerable number of marijuana smokers who have significant psychological and emotional problems. There has been a great deal of discussion, however, concerning which comes first—the marijuana or the emotional difficulties.

The argument is often made that the emotional problems preceed the use of pot. While that may be true, there is ample evidence that such problems tend to be deepened rather than cured by the company of Mary Jane. There also has been growing interest in what is often referred to as an "amotivational" syndrone. This basically refers to marijuana-induced changes of goals and ambitions. A growing number of researchers are contending that while marijuana may seldom be the sole cause of personality change, it is at least a very significant factor in many cases. The extreme, of course, of such changes is the individual who decides that the passive, contemplative state which marijuana frequently produces is preferable to living with reality. Pot, for that person, soon becomes the center of existence.

Effects on Society

The impact that marijuana will have on society is only beginning to be measured. If substantial physical problems are discovered, then society will pay greatly for its use. If it causes increasing psychological withdrawal from a world that desperately needs productive talent, then the price will be high. The reformer, not the recluse, is the great need of the world today. While only the future can tell us what the costs will be, there are some immediate social concerns that deserve at least brief attention.

Does "Cannabis" Lead to Crime?

Practically all of the serious investigators who have attempted to examine this question have found no significant relationship between marijuana and major crime. The records of the Bureau of Narcotics and Dangerous Drugs hold a few cases of felony crimes performed by people supposedly having marijuana-induced psychoses.

The characteristic passive reaction to marijuana may even tend to inhibit rather than cause violence. The most significant drug used by delinquents is alcohol. The "pot heads" tend to be far less aggressive than the "boozers."

Do "Highs" Lead to Heroin?

The "stepping-stone" theory has received wide attention and fairly general acceptance in the United States. The theory is that once a person has had an initial experience with a rather mild drug such as marijuana, he will tend to move on to the harder and more dangerous drugs. Opponents of the theory point to the

AUSTIN (UPI)—A psychiatrist and researcher told a legislative committee this week that 30 to 50 per cent of Texas' high school students have smoked marijuana and said he has new evidence that pot causes brain abnormalities.

Dr. Robert B. White, professor of psychiatry at the University of Texas medical branch in Galveston, said tests over the past six months on cats have shown that injections of marijuana extract causes definite abnormalities in brain patterns that persist after regular doses are administered for 8 to 10 days.

fact that although marijuana use has sky-rocketed in the last five years, the number of heroin addicts has remained fairly static. Such an argument, it would seem, lacks validity at several points. First, in the last year or so the use of heroin has begun to rise substantially. Dr. Donald Louria has observed that a heroin epidemic has hit New York. Other experts have indicated fears that the number of heroin addicts may mushroom from 25,000 in New York to 100,000 in a year or so.

Secondly, there is indication that while marijuana users may not often turn to heroin, they do turn to the stronger hallucinogens, the uppers and the downers. People who are inclined to lean heavily on marijuana frequently have a definite transfer mechanism which tends to lead them to more destructive substances. Further, the marijuana user is usually encouraged by his peers and by pushers to go on to harder drugs. A youngster in a group smoking grass is likely to hear, "Man, if you think that is good, you ought to try hash." If he thinks the hash is good, then "speed" would be even better. The drug culture is a culture which encourages the progressive use of drugs and the pot smoker is at least to some extent a part of that culture.

Is It Safe to Drive with Marijuana?

Practically no significant attention has been given to this question which is certainly an important one in our motorized society. One study, which can hardly be considered valid, was conducted by the Bureau of Motor Vehicles in the State of Washington. The results showed little impairment of driving ability. Subjects, however, smoked as long as 30 minutes to get "high," which indicates that they probably received extremely small doses. The best effects are obtained from rapid, deep smoking. Also, the investigators waited another hour before beginning the testings. Most of the effects of a mild "high" will usually have dissipated in half that length of time. Further, the subjects had been given a number of practice runs before pot was used and practically knew the simulation by memory by the time the "high" tests took place.

Pot smokers themselves, aware of the tendency of time and space distortion, generally say that they would not want to drive while high. This should at least indicate that great caution should be exercised before this nation allows pot smokers to join those drinking drivers who are involved in at least 50 per cent of the nation's traffic accidents.

Marijuana will continue to be a symbol of the frustration and rebellion of American youth. Sympathy for legalization will probably grow. But the young person must confront some serious questions. How valuable is his future? How valuable is his home? How valuable is his mind and body? If he considers these to have value, then there is cause to think twice before using marijuana. What is known is serious. What is not known might be even more serious.

4

LSD: A TRIP
TO WHERE?

(By William S. Garmon)

Who among us does not know what the letters LSD represent? Maybe we can't pronounce the name d-lysergic acid diethylamide, but we have heard about "acid," to use the hippie phrase. We know it can do strange things to users. Most people have heard the claims made for the effects of the drug—mind-expanding, creative impetus, a mental state of great calm, intense pleasure, etc., but more of us are now also hearing of some terrible possible side effects, particularly the side effects of flashbacks from bad trips.

Art Linkletter, one of the better-known and respected men of the entertainment field, like many other parents was brought face to face with the drug problem when it invaded his home. On October 4, 1969 Diane Linkletter, the youngest daughter of the family, plunged to her death from her tenth floor Hollywood apartment building. The death was labeled a suicide. The matter could have rested at this point, but Linkletter and his family decided that it must not because Diane was experiencing a recurrence of an earlier bad trip while on LSD. Art Linkletter and his family rather than hiding from the public in their grief decided to attempt to do something about the drug problem, otherwise Diane's death was in vain. Linkletter discovered he was not alone for thousand of letters sharing personal experiences began to pour into his office. It can happen to us, to our families.

The Hallucinogens

"Psychedelic" has now become a new descriptive word in the language. It refers, first, to a type of hallucinogenic drugs, but often to a type of music or a combination of colors both in paintings and in wearing apparel. The latter is no real problem, but it is important to know something about the drugs.

LSD is a colorless, odorless, tasteless liquid or powder, that is, in the pure state. As it is sold, it can come in many forms. It is probably the most powerful of the class of drugs known as

---

ARLINGTON, Va. (AP)—A $500,000 shipment of cocaine was seized by federal agents Wednesday in a raid of an Arlington apartment. Six persons were arrested.

Brian P. Getting, U. S. attorney for the eastern district of Virginia, said two kilograms of cocaine were confiscated at what was described as a transfer point in an Atlantic coast narcotics ring. (Associated Press, March 5, 1970.)

---

hallucinogens. It was first synthesized in 1938 by the Swiss chemist Albert Hufmann. The mind-altering effects were accidentaly discovered some years later.

Basically LSD along with the other drugs in this class are considered investigational drugs. However, two or three plants contain chemicals which are hallucinogenic and have long been used. Some authorities list marijuana as one of these while others insist that it is more like alcohol or even narcotic-like. Psilocybin and psilocin are drugs derived from plants—mushrooms generally grown in Mexico. Mescaline is derived from the buttons of the peyote plant and has been used by Indians for centuries in religious ceremonies. A weak hallucinogen related to LSD has been extracted from certain varieties of morning glory seeds. These have long been used, but are not currently popular.

DMT, a short-acting hallucinogen, is derived from the seeds of a plant native to the West Indies and South America. Bufotenine is related chemically to DMT and is derived from dried glandular secretions of a certain toad and also from a fungus. Both of these drugs can also be produced synthetically. Ibogaine is derived from an African vine. DET and DOM (STP) are synthetics.

Tripping

The word "trip" has taken on a new connotation in the language with the appearance of the drug cultists. One is said to be on a trip while under the influence of the psychedelics. The particular reaction an individual will have from taking a hallucinogen is often quite subjective. At least three factors are always involved in the effects of drugtaking: the amount and the quality of the drug involved, the psychological and physiological factors of the user, and the social and cultural context. Enough persons have reported the effects of taking the hallucinogens that a reasonably accurate picture can be formed.

The usual dosage of LSD is 100 micrograms, an amount which could be held on the end of a sharp pencil lead and could not be seen by the naked human eye. It will take effect within one-half hour, and the effects normally last about ten hours. LSD affects the central nervous system so that there is a distortion in the perception of color, light, sound, and material or animate objects. A catalogue of the full range of effects would include mood changes, anxiety, distortion of perception, hallucinations, delusions, and depersonalization.

Apparently the primary effect of the drug is a modification of one's understanding of reality—another dimension of reality is made manifest. The alleged enchantment of the senses is proba-

---

LOS ANGELES (AP)—For $8,000 a group of hippies has been hired by a school district to conduct an in-school drug education program.

The self-described hippies and former drug users have been meeting with students, parents, teachers and community leaders for six weeks in the Paramount School District. They will be in the community three more weeks. (Associated Press, February 22, 1970.)

---

bly the effect most cited. The senses appear to be sharpened and heightened. On the one hand color takes on a fantastic brightness and depth, hearing becomes abnormally acute; on the other hand there is a blending and diffusion of the senses so that color is tasted, sounds are felt, and inaminate objects pulsate and breathe. There is a wide range of emotions with marked fluctuations. Closely related to this reaction is a sense of changes in perception of space and time. An object in the distance may become very close. Time may stand still or rush rapidly forward. Limbs and facial features may become grossly distorted. There is a tendency to identify with the environment and to become one with the universe so that depersonalization occurs. However, the psychedelics are not truly hallucinogens, for hallucinations have no reality except in the imagination, but that a similar effect is produced is obvious.

About four to eight milligrams of psilocybin are needed to produce illusions or hallucinations for a five to twelve hour period. A dose of 350 to 500 milligrams of mescaline is needed to produce a trip. STP is only about one-tenth as strong as LSD, but when taken in large doses it can give prolonged and intense reactions. (STP is, as one of my students insisted on an exam, the brand name for a petroleum product, but here we are concerned with the drug.) DMT tends to give a blast as the mind-expanding effects are short-term and overpowering. This drug can be inhaled from the smoke of the burning seeds or it can be injected. DET is smoked, and STP is usually obtained in tablet form. Bufoteine is generally injected. Of all the hallucinogens, LSD is the most common among drug abusers. Since there is no legal manufacture of the drug, it appears in many forms, but is most likely to be found in tablets.

A Bum Trip

A number of persons have reported bad trips from taking LSD or one of the other hallucinogens. Much of the popular literature has focused on the mind-manifesting aspects of the drug; thus the use of the word "psychedelic," but this term ignores some of the other aspects of the altered system of consciousness produced by the drug. At one time LSD was labeled a psychotomimetic drug, meaning that it produced an imitation of a psychosis. Although the evidence is not all in, the use of the drug can apparently trigger psychoses and even suicide many weeks or months after the original trip. A case in point was Diane Linkletter as mentioned earlier. In a two year period of time over 130 patients were admitted to Bellevue Hospital in New York suffering from acute psychoses or chronic schizophrenia from bad trips. Whereas the drug normally wears off within about ten hours, some persons continue to hallucinate at times for weeks without again taking the drug.

Besides the psychological effects of LSD, an increasing number of researchers have become convinced that abuse can produce long term physical damage. Scientists have discovered abnormal chromosomal patterns in persons who have taken LSD, and some scattered reports of deformed babies being born to users have been recorded. Young people have lost their lives

---

FAIRFAX (AP)—Five persons have been arrested in raids in which city and county police said they confiscated one of the largest collections of drugs in Northern Virginia history.

Two predawn raids Friday, one in the city and the other in the county, resulted in the seizure of $15,000 worth of hashish and $10,000 in cash.

Also uncovered, police said, were a quantity of cocaine, marijuana and LSD, plus weapons and passports. (Associated Press, March 21, 1970.)

---

by walking in front of speeding automobiles and subway trains in the belief that no harm would come to them. Others have stepped out of windows in the belief that they could fly.

Some trips are mixed, that is, the individual will experience a heightened sense of perception of sound, color, taste, etc., but then lapse into feelings of panic, paranoia, fear, violent impulses, suicidal thoughts, and feelings of isolation. Not enough research has been done for us to know all of the real long-term effects of taking the hallucinogenic drugs, but enough is known to label LSD a dangerous drug. Tolerance does develop. Long term usage requires increased dosage to obtain the desired effects. While LSD is not physically addicting, psychological dependence does develop. The Federal Government and over half of the states have laws which attempt to control the traffic in the drug. Since LSD is odorless, colorless, and tasteless, it is most difficult to detect. It can be transported in a sugar cube, a pill, a capsule, mixed with the glue on an envelope flap, or in blotter paper. It can also be readily made in a home laboratory. After widespread publicity was given to chromosomal damage discovered in users, there was an apparent decline in usage. However, at the time of this writing marijuana is in short supply, and it is thought that some of the young are turning again to the more powerful LSD.

Psychedelic Creativity

Any judgment on what contribution the psychedelic cult has made to culture is purely relative. Commercial forces were quick to seize on the value of the alleged influence in art, the theater, music, and wearing apparel. Acid rock is big in the popular music field. Several performing groups have names which tie with the drug scene. Some song titles or words play on the use of LSD or marijuana, although this is sometimes denied. Long hair, beads, strobe lights, the use of flourishes, spirals, and curlicues in camouflaged tones, or the playing of purples against blues or reds against pinks—the whole hippie scene—has been commercialized. Young or old may participate in the scene vicariously.

There is apparently a difference in what one sees under the influence of LSD and what one can actually write, draw, or otherwise produce under the influence or what can be recorded from memory after the effects have worn off. Actual clinical tests in painting and writing do not bear out the claims made for creativity. Subjects have been found to perform about the same or even worse under the influence of the psychedelics.

History has a way of repeating itself. Claims made today for the mind-expanding effects of LSD and marijuana were made earlier for other substances such as alcohol, opium, chloroform, ether, and nitrous oxide (laughing gas). What are now considered routine, commonplace drugs to be used in unromantic ways were once crowned with a mystic aura.

Have the new combinations and the imaginative uses of colors and sounds been produced by persons taking a drug or have they been accomplished by creative imaginations acting on ideas from a wide variety of sources? Someone has pointed out that Dali is the best psychedelic painter of all, but he never took a trip. There is quite a difference between genuine creativity and what one feels or thinks to be creative. Does creativity come out of preparation, frustration, chance, or perspiration?

Chemical Religion

At least one scientist theorizes that a holy plant tied to an early form of the Hindu religion may have contained a hallucinogenic drug. It is the contention that the remembrance of the experience of hallucination led to a strictly physical way of producing ecstasy. Over a century prior to the discovery of

---

NEW YORK (AP)—A youth testified at a state legislative committee hearing on drug addiction yesterday about his heroin addiction and how he supported it. The witness sat on his doctor's lap while he spoke.

"I used to see all my friends do it, so I didn't want to be left out," a 12 year-old boy named Ralph said as he explained to the committee how he turned to heroin after sniffing glue and cleaning fluid and smoking marijuana.

The 4-foot-tall, 60-pound addict said he sold drugs to adults and other youngsters at a Bronx elementary school, and also supported his habit by stealing purses, breaking into stores and helping older friends mug people. (Associated Press, February 27, 1970.)

LSD, Indian groups in Mexico and in the United States were using peyote buttons. These are still in use. The Indians cut off and dry the cactus tops. The "buttons" are eaten in night-long ceremonies accompanied with sacred fire and chanting. Mescaline, the natural chemical, is not so powerful as the synthetic LSD, but it does fall into the category of a hallucinogen. The use of this drug by Indians was long suppressed, but its use in religious services was legalized in New Mexico in the year 1959. Under the Federal Drug Abuse Act of 1965 the Native American Church was permitted to use the peyote buttons in religious worship. Recent court decisions have refused to extend this privilege to other groups.

Dr. Timothy Leary was very much in the news in recent years. He was one of the early experimenters with LSD and was fired from his position at Harvard when he began to involve undergraduate students in his experiments with mind-expanding drugs. A young investment banker provided Leary with a rather large country estate which served as headquarters for the League of Spiritual Discovery. LSD is considered a sacred biochemical which clears the path to mystic understanding. Divinity is, however, sought within the person. It was Leary who tied the ancient goals of religion to the modern slogan: "Turn on, tune in, and drop out."

Leary's connection of a chemical to religious experience was not new. No less a person than William James, whose *Varieties of Religious Experience* is a classic, quite often tied the use of drugs with religious experience. Many users of LSD have recounted a sense of oneness with the universe. Divinity is seen as being within. God is seen as life, and since the user is life, he is God. Ego identity is lost. I suspect that one can experience the same feeling from oxygen deprivation.

While LSD trips are usually taken with a friend, continued use tends to make one less responsive to the needs of others. Examination of pictures of groups using LSD shows isolation and withdrawal rather than community. Individuals are turned inward rather than outward. Long-term users of the drug become more and more unconcerned about the world around them. This is explained by emphasizing that the mystical insight gained through LSD makes the goals one has been working for seem no longer worth pursuing. Rather than making one more loving as the drug cultists claim, continued use of LSD tends to make one less capable of loving.

FAYETTEVILLE, N. C. (AP)—"Body feelings are about the first thing you notice; I mean, like, almost a compulsion to laugh and it's all inside your chest—and then your head, you get kind of a numb feeling, I mean, like there's nothing there.

"Then you start noticing these little things going on around you and it seems like you're kind of super-sensitive; I mean, everything is real tense and a lot of times you get in a kind of a paranoid feeling, that somebody is watching you or something like that. . . ."

These are the words of an 18-year-old youth who is in Cumberland County jail facing trial for possessing LSD for the purpose of sale. (Associated Press, November 10, 1968.)

Responsible Faith

Turning-on, tuning-in, and dropping-out hardly meets the test of resonsibility, whether from the Christian or secularist viewpoint. A generation caught in existential despair which feels alienation, aloneness, estrangement, and which is trying to find an identity can present a real challenge to the Christian faith. Man by his nature seeks God or gods. Man cannot see himself as he is until he sees God as he is. Isaiah 6:1–8 records an experience of the prophet with God which is most instructive. When the prophet saw the Lord as he was—high and lifted up, he saw himself as he was—a man of unclean lips dwelling with a people who were the same. God was recognized as the maker, lover, and keeper of all life. He was transcendent, yet present in his creation. When the prophet realized his own uncleanness he asked for and received immediate cleansing. The response was automatic—a positive response which came out of gratitude.

LOS ANGELES (AP)—A hallucinogenic drug—believed to be LSD or something similar—that was secretly sprinkled on potato and corn chips at a weekend party sent 27 guests to the hospital.

"Some of the people were acting as though they were drugged or intoxicated," said Sheriff's Deputy James Lyle. "Some of them were staring, some were unusually happy, some were sick.

Some were screaming, some said the walls were moving, others were staring into space. One man cried that his hands were getting bigger." (Associated Press, April 6, 1970.)

The prophet responded to the call of God in awe, adoration, gratitude, thanksgiving, and praise. Worship is a time of introspection, confession, involvement, and self-surrender. It is only in an experience such as this that man can be free from the tyranny of the self and accept his true being.

Whereas the theme of the psychedelic cult is defeatist and irresponsible, Christian love is not impersonal, pleasure-seeking, or egocentric, but personal, responsible, and involved. The Christian passion always involves a cross; and, man, if he is to be called Christian, must be prepared to accept it.

The use of LSD and other hallucinogens threatens to become a social problem of greater magnitude than the use of opiates. The use of the drug spread rapidly with the flowering of the hippie movement, and experimentation with LSD has now become a problem in some high schools and in some areas even to younger children.

The indirect effects of experimentation with psychedelic drugs have been far-reaching in the fields of music, art, and religion. Research in the possible medical uses for the drug continues particularly with alcoholics and terminal cancer patients. LSD came on the scene at that moment in history when many Americans were ready to reach out to anything which offered a modification of harsh reality. For some experimenters, the cure has become worse than the disease.

5

GRADUATING
TO THE HARD STUFF

(By William S. Garmon)

Not all of the persons who start experimenting with marijuana, LSD, or pills of various hues will eventually go to heroin. However, most users of narcotics started on something much milder. This is true of upwards of seventy-five to ninety percent, and the majority of these started with marijuana.

The addict is generally viewed as one of the most reprehensible individuals on the face of the earth. However, attitudes are shifting somewhat and the addict is seen by some in the category of the alcoholic, the homosexual, or the sociopath, that is, a person who is in need of help. Yet there is not much sympathy for the addict in many communities. He is seen as a person who brought on his own illness, if it can be viewed as an illness or disease. Rest assured that the majority of addicts are sick in body and spirit. They are junkies. They need and must have junk to keep going and they will sell their souls, if necessary, to obtain it. As William S. Burroughs has graphically stated, "You see junk *is* a personality—a seedy gray man; a rooming house; a shabby street; a room on the top floor; stairs; cough; . . . bathroom with yellow wood panels, dripping toilet, works stashed under the wash basin; back in his room now cooking up. A gray shadow on a distant wall—that used to be me, mister." [1]

Narcotics

The term narcotic is often misused in common parlance. It is invoked to cover pills of all varieties, any drug which is commonly abused. The opiate is the drug which is of major concern, however, in a discussion of the narcotic addict. The opiates include some derivatives—morphine, codeine, paragoric, and heroin. Opium was known to the Egyptians as early as 1500 B.C. Heroin is a much more sophisticated drug which was first synthesized about 1898 from a morphine base. The process is rather simple. It involves treating the morphine or opium base with acetic acid to form diacetylmorphine or heroin. Interestingly enough it was called "heroin" from hero. When first discovered it was thought to be non-addicting. The drug was going to solve many problems and was thus the hero.

The opiates have a long history of use in the medical field.

NEW YORK (AP)—A 17-year-old boy died of a narcotics overdose Saturday, the 34th teenager to die of drug abuse in the city this year . . . .

So far this week, five teenagers have died of drug overdoses in the city.

Last year, the city reported 900 drug deaths, 224 of them teenagers. (Associated Press, February 22, 1970.)

Heroin, however, is so highly addicting that it is not used in medical practice in the United States. The drug is a white, buff, or brown powder which is generally used by injection. It is a depressant which works on the central nervous system inducing euphoria, grogginess, incoordination, and impaired thought processes. It is the euphoria, of course, which is sought by the addict. Depending on the strength of the product, the supply of heroin in the United States ranges in purity from one to thirty percent, one dose per day for a period of a month can produce addiction. Tolerance builds rapidly, that is, the addict may need ever-increasing doses to produce the euphoria desired. However, it should be pointed out that the addict is not really addicted until he ties the euphoria and the drug together. Psychological factors also operate. Many of the alleged addicts are really addicted to the needle, that is, the stuff they are getting is of such poor quality that they can scarcely be said to be addicted to the heroin. This is one of the reasons why there are many deaths from overdosage. If an addict has been shooting relatively poor-grade heroin and suddenly gets some relatively pure stuff, he can easily overdose and the curtain falls unexpectedly. Pushers don't worry about quality control, only the fast buck.

The physical action of heroin on the body can literally wreck it. Symptoms of addiction include constipation, loss of appetite with subsequent malnutrition, loss of sex drive, and a lowering of the respiration rate. (The image of the drug-crazed sex maniac is all fabrication.)

Addiction in the young, and most addicts are young, may not be readily detected because of the amazing recuperative powers of the youthful body. Marked mental and physical deterioration may not be apparent until usage has been extensive. Symptoms of narcotic use among the young would include: drowsiness and yawning, general apathy, discolored whites of eyes, watery eyes, enlargement of the pupils, antisocial or abnormal ideas, lessened effect of the moral sense, restlessness, facial or body spasms, stomach sensitive to food intake, and hypodermic marks, sores, scabs, scar-tissue, or marked discolorations. The most common

---

FRANKFORT, Ky. (AP)—A Kentucky Crime Commission conference of police officials from throughout the state has proposed a law against motorists under the influence of narcotics—similar to drunken driving statutes. (Associated Press, March 28, 1970.)

---

place to introduce the drug into the body is on the inner-side of the elbow; however, any surface blood vessel of the arm may be used. For that matter any part of the body can be used, but the arm is the most common. Some youngsters inject the drug under the tongue where the needle will not leave tracks which will be visible. Most addicts will wear long-sleeved shirts to prevent detection of "tracks" on their arms. They may also mask these by burns, cuts, or other skin abrasions.

The "works" used for shooting heroin, the most common form of narcotics abused, usually consist of a hypodermic needle, syringe or eye dropper, a bottle cap or spoon for heating liquid, cotton for straining the liquid, and a piece of rubber tubing or other material for use as a tourniquet. The favored technique of injecting varies from one geographic area to another.

The addict is subject to bronchitis and other diseases of the respiratory system, particularly since heroin depresses the cough reflex and the lungs tend to fill with mucus. The inability of the addict to feel pain can lead to serious physical injury such as burns, bruises, etc. It is not uncommon to see an addict with the meat burned off several finger tips. Hepatitis and tetanus are often transmitted by the use of unsterile equipment for injection of the drugs or by contaminants contained in the illicit supply. Last year some of the caps sold in the Washington area were found to contain a cleansing agent normally used to clean the kitchen sink. Adulterants are usually added to impart the bitter taste which good heroin is supposed to possess and to make the pharmacological effects of the heroin more potent. Quinine or methapyrilene is often used to dilute the white heroin, while the brownish heroin is frequently adulterated with crystalline procaine.

The addict is literally hooked on drugs and will go to extreme lengths to prevent the occurrence of withdrawal symptoms. Once addicted, the user seeks the euphoria of the drugged state. Preventing the pains of withdrawal becomes a life obsession. The extent of suffering involved in kicking the narcotic varies with the individual and the quality and quantity of the drug used. Withdrawal is generally marked by light fever, watery and burning eyes, hot and cold flashes, leg and stomach cramps, goose flesh, diarrhea, insomnia, prostration, and in some cases circulatory collapse and/or shock. These can be so severe as to cause death. The intensity of the pain involved in the withdrawal usually peaks within twenty-four to forty-eight hours, but some of the symptoms may continue for weeks. The latter stages are generally marked by deep depression. The problem of getting rid of the physical addiction is not nearly so difficult as removing the psychological addiction.

NEW YORK (AP)—A Bronx grand jury has indicted two men on charges of manslaughter and criminally negligent homicide in connection with the heroin-sniffing death of a Barnard College coed.

In announcing the indictments Wednesday, Bronx Dist. Atty. Burton B. Roberts said he knew of no other instance in which manslaughter and homicide statutes had been used against drug suppliers in connection with narcotics deaths of willing users. (Associated Press, February 26, 1970.)

Who Are They?

At the end of 1967 the Bureau of Narcotics had records of 62,045 opiate addicts in the United States, ninety percent of whom were on heroin. Since the list is compiled from records voluntarily reported to the agency, and since not all addicts come into contact with police or health agencies, the number is merely an estimate.

Dr. William Bloom, Jr., in a recent study of drug addiction in the city of New Orleans, Louisiana, estimated that there were at least a thousand hard-core addicts in the city. He actually discovered 609 cases, yet at that time the Bureau of Narcotics listed Louisiana as having only 206 active cases in the state. The problem is obviously much larger than the statistics of known addicts indicate it to be. How much larger no one really knows.

Essentially addicts are young people, mostly males between the ages of the late teens and the late twenties. The heroin addict is usually described as being found in a large urban area. In fact over one-half of the known addicts live in the area of New York city. The problem has been basically one of the inner-city slums where the poorly educated, unskilled, and disadvantaged minority groups live. Well over one-half of the known addicts are Negroes and Puerto Ricans. The addict usually feels hopeless and helpless and uses drugs as a way of opting out of normal society.

There is some evidence that the entire picture of heroin use is changing. Marijuana use and the use of pills range up and down the social ladder. Currently the indications are that heroin usage is moving out of the ghettos, up the social ladder, and into the early teen years. Recent estimates indicate that New York city alone will have 100,000 addicts by the end of the year. Most of these will be in their teens or at most in the early twenties. With marijuana becoming increasingly difficult to obtain and with young people being increasingly able to obtain money there are some real possibilities that heroin use is on the upswing. Whereas the rate of addiction had been steadily declining since the Civil war, it is definitely increasing at present. Just how rapidly is not known.

It is generally conceded that heroin abusers have dependent personalities. Drug-taking is seen as an effort to compensate for feelings of inferiority and insecurity. However, most medical authorities contend that anyone who uses heroin regularly for a few weeks will become addicted even if he is exceptionally mature in personality and in the best state of mental health. Indeed, some addicts are medical addicts, that is, they started on drugs when there was a legitimate reason to do so.

Once addicted to heroin, the addict thinks of little else but getting the fix. Life is now built around keeping a supply of the precious drug. There are a few integrated addicts, that is, persons who can work at a regular job and supply their drug needs.

MIAMI (AP)—A caravan named Right-A-Wrong has begun a five-month schedule of one-night stands across the United States to drum up support for a national referendum to legalize marijuana.

"Primarily we aim to capture, or at least reach, the older person—the postcollege or non-college persons between 30 and 40 and even 51," said Stuart Arrow, 24, its national co-ordinator. (Associated Press, February 7, 1970.)

Most addicts, however, find it impossible to maintain a normal work pattern; thus they turn to crime in order to supply their habit.

What Are the Costs?

Addicts commit a staggering amount of crime against property, crime largely designed to raise funds. Contrary to popular opinion, addiction itself is not a crime, but being caught with the drugs on the person is. The addict must raise the money for his habit and it is expensive. Women tend to go into prostitution, men tend to steal, forge checks, or become pushers. Since stolen property must be traded through a fence, between three and five dollars of merchandise is required to obtain a dollar in cash. An addict on a fifteen-dollars-a-day habit would by necessity steal merchandise worth at least fifty dollars each day. The price of heroin varies from city to city and from one period of time to another, but the fifteen-dollars-a-day cost is about average for the nation. There are no holidays from drug use. This means that the addict will spend $5,475 per year for drugs. Some addicts are on one-hundred-dollars-a-day habits. Their costs are astronomical. Even the average addict who is supporting his habit by stealing will by necessity steal $18,250 worth of merchandise each year. Even allowing for the fact that some addicts enter prostitution, a few manage to work and support their habit, and others become pushers, it is safe to estimate that addicts steal over a billion dollars worth of property each year.

Treatment programs are expensive. On the average it probably cost $2,000 a year just to maintain an addict in jail. Short-term inpatient treatment followed by intensive after care will

SAN BERNARDINO, Calif. (AP)—A Municipal Court judge has ruled that a narcotics search in a baby's diaper by sheriff's deputies was unconstitutional because the baby didn't consent. (Associated Press, February 1, 1970.)

run about $3,000 or more per year. Even so, a treatment program for all of the addicts in the United States would not be as expensive as the present property loss due to crime committed by addicts.

Most of the traffic in illicit opiates is under the control of organized crime. This has not been true of the traffic in marijuana and LSD because there has not been enough money in these items. However, in recent months the price of marijuana has gone up because of the limited supply coming into the country. There are some indications that the supply routes are becoming more regular and better organized. The crime syndicates could well move into this operation.

Consider the staggering financial possibilities in the illicit heroin traffic. One kilogram (2.2 pounds) of pure refined heroin, distributed to the addicts in the United States, will bring close to one-quarter of a million dollars. Wholesale heroin bought in New York or Mexico will cost about $350 per ounce. (It can run much higher, depending on the level of the supplies in the United States.) The original ounce will be diluted four or five times and from each of these diluted ounces about three hundred caps can be made. These sell for about five dollars on the street. Of course the heroin may be cut more than five times. Analysis of caps bought on the street will show a heroin content of from about thirty per cent at best to as little as one per cent. Most caps will range at the two to four per cent level. This indicates that a lot of addicts supply their need by cutting their own supply.

No one really knows how much heroin is smuggled into the United States each year. Most of it comes originally from Turkey or the Far East, but some enters from Mexico. Last year the U. S. Custom's inspectors collected 54,818 pounds of heroin, opium, hashish, marijuana, cocaine, and other narcotics from 3,425 travelers entering the states. How much escaped the customs net? Who knows? The department is grossly understaffed.

What Hope for the Addict?

Apparently it is most difficult to get an addict to give up the habit. The recovery rate is actually not known, but it is thought to be quite poor. This is one reason why parents and authorities become quite upset as the addiction rate climbs. Few long-term studies of addict recovery rates have been made. Because the addicts live to get drugs and getting drugs becomes life itself, many addicts completely ignore their physical welfare. Many die young as current statistics in news accounts coming out of New

GREENSBORO (AP)—About 10 drug addicts a month wash out of a federal rehabilitation program in Lexington, Ky., after being sent there for a cure by U. S. Middle District Court in Greensboro.

The disappointing rejection rate has prompted Asst. U. S. Atty. Howard Cable to call the program a "total failure," though the federal law setting it up in 1966 drew widespread professional approval as a breakthrough in combatting addiction.

The law, the Narcotics Addict Rehabilitation Act, was greeted by doctors, psychiatrists and social workers as the first official recognition that drug addiction is a disease as well as a crime. (Associated Press, March 20, 1970.)

York indicate. Others take "the cure" only to relapse within a short time. Some spend much of their lives in jails because, once caught selling drugs or in possession of drugs, they usually face heavy penalties. However, there is some evidence to indicate that if an addict survives long enough he will probably "mature" out of the addiction. If they survive long enough, and this is a big if, apparently the majority of addicts will realize that they are headed down a one-way street and seek help.

Since 1935 the United States Public Health Service has treated over eighty thousand addicts in two hospitals, one located in Lexington, Kentucky and the other in Fort Worth, Texas. The hospitals were originally designed primarily for the treatment of federal prisoners, but about one-half of the patients at any given time have been persons who voluntarily entered the facilities for treatment of addiction. Most of the volunteers do not remain for the full five-month treatment period recommended, but leave against medical advice. Currently new facilities for treatment of federal prisoners are being opened. How successful the treatment program has been at Lexington and Fort Worth is a matter of debate. Persons who left the hospital under some form of compulsory supervision after discharge seem to succeed more often than those under no restraint. In one study of one hundred patients who had been discharged over a twelve year period of time, ninety of the one hundred had returned to drug use at some time; however, forty-six of them were drug-free in the community at the time of death or at the period of last contact.

Withdrawal from heroin under proper medical superivison is not exceedingly dangerous nor necessarily even extremely painful. Some addicts do withdraw voluntarily by the "cold turkey" method. Keeping the addict from returning to drugs involves more than just getting the heroin out of the system. Removing the psychological need for drugs is at times most difficult. While it is inadvisable to look for an "addict prone personality," most addicts do prove to be insecure and immature. However, these conditions are not always apparent.

NEW YORK (AP)—Authorities say a father of four who was arrested on drug charges used teams of children to peddle narcotics . . . .

The three (children) told police they each sold an average of 90 bags of heroin at $10 a piece every day and each cleared about $50 daily. The rest went to the collector. (Associated Press, January 30, 1970.)

Increasingly it is being recognized that little is to be gained by sending the addict to prison. The trend is toward civil commitment of the addict to a treatment center. The earliest state program did not come into existence until 1961 in California. Federal legislation was passed in 1966. At this point it is impossible to know whether experiments with rehabilitation of addicts rather than punishment will be successful, although many authorities have raised serious questions. Enough is known to indicate that these programs are not magic panaceas. The hue and cry is still heard, "Throw them under the jails, particularly the pushers." Certainly the treatment of the user and the seller should be different; however, these often become the same person. It is difficult at times to distinguish between the two. The pusher who is in the business because of his habit should be treated differently from the pusher who is in the traffic for the money. Interestingly enough most of the suppliers are not addicts. The wholesalers, the organized criminal element, these are the ones who certainly should be locked away. They are the ones who are capitalizing on human misery.

A fuller discussion of the treatment programs which seem to offer some hope for assisting the addict will be presented in the next chapter of this book. As Christians, we do have a responsibility to support law enforcement officers in their efforts to stop the traffic in illicit drugs. It is also vital that we support the experimental programs which are designed to rehabilitate the addict. It is this writers opinion that it is desirable to support legislation aimed at civil commitment rather than imprisonment as an end in itself. We must be concerned about what we can do to remove the conditions of hopelessness and despair which create a climate for drug use. We must become involved in the problem. The lives we save may be those of our own children.

Drug addiction is presently a grave social problem which threatens to become larger. While the number of addicts is small in comparison to the number of persons addicted to alcohol, the concomitant social consequences are sizeable. Illicit drugs are expensive. The astronomical profits involved feed organized crime. The rehabilitation rate is low. Working for the physical and spiritual redemption of addicts may be optional for some segments of society, but for the Christian it is mandatory.

NOTES

1. William S. Burroughs, "Kicking Drugs: A Very Personal Story," *Harper's Magazine,* 236 (July, 1967), p. 40.

6
GETTING THE MONKEY
OFF HIS BACK
(By Phil Strickland)

It is difficult to know how to respond to the person who has already substantially damaged his life. It is particularly difficult when that person does not look, smell or talk like one is "supposed" to. The Christian believes, however, that there is always the possibility that life can be redeemed.

A new life begins for the narcotic addict only when he is able to get off of drugs. He then must readjust to a non-drug life which many addicts have not known for a long time. But where does the addict go for such a beginning? What treatment is available and where can it be found?

Facilities for drug treatment have expanded rapidly in the last few years. Some of the programs have received national attention. Others are relatively obscure. This chapter can only briefly examine a few of the alternatives now available. Before turning to specific programs, however, it is important to consider one preliminary question.

Is there any hope for the real addict, the "junkie?" Is he doomed to spend the rest of his life with an addiction which can never be cured? Many have concluded that the answers are affirmative. But among those who work with addicts, there is an increasing optimism about the chances of many addicts returning to normal, productive life.

It is true that virtually all of the treatment programs have had limited success. Many of the quoted relapse rates are very discouraging. The United States unit at Lexington, Kentucky, for example, indicates that about 95 per cent of the people discharged use heroin again within six months. But Dr. Louria suggests that the picture is not as dim as it first seems. Another follow-up about five years later, however, shows a voluntary abstinence rate of up to 25 per cent. While those are still poor odds for the parent whose child is an addict, it at least gives cause for hope. Studies have also been published by Drs. Lee Robins and George Murphy that indicate that as many as 80 per cent of heroin addicts may "grow out" of their addiction by their mid-30's. The figure may be optimistic, but it at least indicates that the addict may eventually "outgrow" his problem —if he lives long enough!

Hundreds, perhaps thousands, of treatment facilities now exist. Many more are needed. Generally, the programs fall into three categories: narcotic maintenance treatment, privately supported programs and treatment supported by state and federal government.

Narcotic Maintenance

Narcotic maintenance programs have been known and used for years. This system of treatment is based on the premise that heroin addiction is a sickness and should not be considered a crime. Thus, physicians should be allowed to prescribe maintenance doses of the drug itself. The United States experimented with a "clinic" approach in the 1920's. Also referred to as "ambulatory treatment," the system allowed patients to go to clinics and get "serviced" whenever they needed maintenance doses. The plan was discontinued after a few years mainly because of the objection of the American Medical Association. The Association noted that the plan was subject to deception and misuse and caused increased abuse of habit-forming drugs.

The "British System" is the same type of approach, but it, too, has been widely misused. Some doctors over-prescribed to certain patients who sold what they did not use. Heroin addiction also rose substantially. Consequently, in 1968 the British government made major revisions in the law so that only certain consultants at specified hospitals could prescribe drugs.

While the "clinic" approach is receiving little contemporary support, another maintenance program is causing great excitement. "Methadone maintenance" is a program which involves switching addicts from heroin, which costs $50 a day or more, to methadone, a synthetic substitue that can be made available for about 15¢ a day. The program was pioneered in New York beginning in 1964 by Drs. Vincent Dole and Marie Nyswander.

Methadone itself is addictive, thus those who use it must either taper off or continue their habit for the rest of their lives. This has caused a great deal of criticism of the program. The critics assert that the goal is to help individuals become self-sufficient with no dependency on any drug. While this is true, it is obvious that there are often times when it is necessary to settle for less than the best. The methadone addict does not have the euphoria or the motor impairment of the heroin addict. Usually, he can turn from crime and take a productive job.

The results of the program have been encouraging. In 1968 one third of those who had participated were considered steadily employed. A second third were either on welfare or employed by the program.

Dr. Louria agrees that the results have been excellent, but points out some important balancing considerations. For instance, the program is only open to volunteers and of those who apply 50 per cent are rejected. This means that those who finally get into the program are highly motivated. Also, the average age of the participants is over thirty, the beginning of the "phasing out" period. Nonetheless, methadone maintenance has worked well and at least provides a means of making life decent again for the addict and society around him.

Private Treatment

The privately run treatment programs have mostly taken the form of small therapeutic communities. Numbers of them have sprung up across the country, but a few have received widespread attention.

Synanon. Begun in 1958 by Charles Dederich, Synanon is a nonmedical approach primarily managed by former addicts. Admission to the program is difficult. A person's desire and will power are tested by such methods as having to show up several times before getting an interview.

The founder, Charles Dederich, developed a number of working premises about addicts. They are: (1) Addicted people should not be blamed for their predicament. (2) They can be praised or punished, but without hostility. (3) The addict is like a child and unable to handle a job or money. (4) Addicts have to be taught love and loyalty, for they have neither. (5) They have no conscience, no morality and no sense of moral responsibility, therefore no blame.

When a person first enters Synanon, he must go through withdrawal without the benefit of medication. The group feels that willingness to do this is an important beginning to rehabilitation. As soon as he is physically able, he will be given a work assignment in the living unit. The first job will be one of the less desirable ones such as scrubbing floors or kitchen clean-up. The sense of community is very strong. Most of the addicts have very little money, so just staying alive with enough to eat is a common concern. There is no paid staff, so members do all of the work.

The crux of the treatment program is the group symposium. Members are encouraged to be completely honest, especially about themselves and each other. The hypothesis is that the addict must give up his façade and be forced to accept himself as he is. The success of this approach has been somewhat limited. Since its beginning Synanon has served over 2000 addicts. Approximately half of these have left before completing the treatment. The majority of the other half have remained at one of the several Synanon centers that now exist. Over 300 have been returned to the community, but follow-up data on these is scant.

There is certainly definite value in the Synanon-type approach. Synanon has not, however, returned significant numbers to community life, even while dealing with highly motivated volunteers. It must be seen as an approach which is needed for some, but not as the one solution to the rehabilitation problem.

Daytop. In 1963 Daytop Lodge was opened on Staten Island, New York, with the aid of a grant from the National Institute of Mental Health. It now has another facility in a rural area in Sullivan County, New York. Daytop is essentially an offshoot of

Synanon, with much of the impetus being provided by David Deitch, an addict who was successfully treated at Synanon. One important distinction from Synanon is that Daytop will accept those referred on probation by the courts as well as volunteers. Group therapy is the center of the rehabilitation program. "Marathon" sessions are frequent wherein a small group of people may confront each other for twenty to thirty hours, hoping that defense mechanisms will collapse as the participants become exhausted.

Over half of the participants drop out before completing the program. Of those who complete the course, the great majority work with Daytop or other addiction treatment programs.

Narcotics Anonymous. Patterned after Alcoholics Anonymous, Narcotics Anonymous was organized in 1948. It seeks to utilize the same theory of rehabilitation that has worked well for Alcoholics Anonymous. Members meet regularly to discuss their problems and provide mutual support. They are asked to apply the principles of Alcoholics Anonymous to their lives.

The success of Narcotics Anonymous has been limited. A number of reasons have been given, but probably the main one is that the kind of open discussion encouraged in the meetings is dangerous for the addict. A vital part of the Alcoholics Anonymous program has been the mutual understanding and support that comes from the sharing of experiences. The addict, however, is afraid that a narcotic agent might be present, thus there is little that he can share without the possibility of making himself and his friends subject to arrest.

Narcotics Anonymous has a companion group called Naranon. This group is designed to meet the needs of relatives by helping them to better understand and relate to addicts. The program is still very small, but seems to have had success where it has been tried. It is one of the few helps available to the families of addicts.

Since few cities have Narcotics Anonymous groups, many addicts attend Alcoholics Anonymous meetings. They find themselves welcome because members of Alcoholics Anonymous also know what it is like to be addicted to something that destroys life. Also, many alcoholics have had experience with drugs. Alcoholics Anonymous is particularly helpful for addicts who have been through treatment and who need support as they adjust to a new life. There is always the knowledge that someone is around to talk to if the temptation to use drugs arises. This is as valuable for the heroin addict as the booze addict.

Teen Challenge. The concern of a pastor for seven boys in trouble led to the beginning of Teen Challenge. In an attempt to help the seven boys who had been indicted for murder, David Wilderson went to New York. While trying to help the boys, David came face to face with the teen-age gangs that roam the streets of New York. Out of his ministry to them came the development in 1968 of a program with headquarters on Clinton Avenue in Brooklyn. There are now centers in several other cities in the United States and Canada and a farm at Rehersburg, Pennsylvania.

Addicts are admitted to Teen Challenge on referrals from courts, doctors, clinics and hospitals. Many of the members are volunteers. Applicants are interviewed by a committee of ministers and rehabilitated addicts to determine their motivation. Only about one in ten is now accepted.

Once in the program, the addict is withdrawn without benefit of medication. Religious experience is at the heart of the rehabilitative program. The staff believes, as David Wilkerson has stated, that "it is impossible to cure a drug addict without God." Consequently, the aim of the group is to impart to the addict a particular kind of religious experience. They believe that once the addict has had such an experience, his life will so change that he will not need drugs. Upon discharge, he is referred to a church which can continue to support him.

There are many programs similar to these scattered throughout the nation. *Encounter,* in New York, *Marathon House,* in Providence, Rhode Island, and others are operated mainly by former drug users. In many instances, however, professional help is being used to complement the program. This provides a needed improvement as there are many problems which former addicts are simply not equipped to handle.

It is important for one to be aware of the facilities available in his area. There are some private mental hospitals that have excellent drug rehabilitation programs. In other places, local hospitals have taken the lead in developing withdrawal and out-patient care facilities. If it is found that a community has no means of treating addicts, then concerned individuals need to move quickly to see that some are developed.

Federal and State Programs

Federal Hospitals. There are two federal hospitals for the treatment of narcotic addiction. One is located at Lexington, Kentucky; the other at Fort Worth, Texas. Both have been in operation since the 1930's. The Lexington hospital will take men from east of the Mississippi and women from anywhere in the United States. The Fort Worth hospital takes only men from west of the Mississippi. Established primarily for the purpose of treating Federal prisoners and probationers, the hospitals also take voluntary patients who are addicted to narcotic drugs as defined by Federal law. This means that someone addicted solely to alcohol or barbiturates is not eligible for admission.

Applications for admission are obtained by writing or calling the hospital. It is preferable, but not absolutely necessary, that the addict be referred by a physician. If accepted, the addict will have to wait until bed space is available.

Once in the hospital, the addict will be withdrawn from his physical addiction with the aid of medication. Methadone is given until the patient is withdrawn from his narcotic addiction. He is then withdrawn from the methadone. The whole process seldom takes more than a week, during which the addict is usually comfortable.

After withdrawal, a broad range of treatments are brought to bear on the addicts' problems. Group therapy is held once a week. Individual counseling is available. Work assignments are given. Vocational training is available, as is schooling at all levels. Together, these aids are supposed to prepare a patient to leave in an "improved" condition in five to ten months.

About one-third of the volunteers sign themselves out before completing withdrawal. Another third leave the first month. Of the final third who stay until discharged, substantially over half will return to the use of drugs. It is difficult, however, to judge the effectiveness of the program on the basis of such figures. Motivation is low. Many of the "volunteers" come to the hospital under pressure from families and friends. Others commit themselves for the primary purpose of getting their habits back under control. These contribute, of course, to the low success rate. Perhaps the main factor, however, is that rehabilitation is done in a vacuum and the readjustments that are made often turn out to be flimsy when they have to bear the return to society. Nonetheless, for some, the hospitals may still be the best hope.

State Programs

It is not surprising to find that the two states which have put the most effort into developing drug rehabilitation programs are New York and California. California in 1961 established a civil committment program for addicts. The addict is sent to a rehabilitation center located in Carona for group psychotherapy, vocational training, remedial education and counseling for both patients and their families. Staff members guide daily group therapy sessions which constitute the heart of the rehabilitation program.

Perhaps the most progressive aspect of the program is the provision for out-patient care. After being released, the addict is kept under supervision by a parole officer who has a maximum case-load of thirty. If the treatment was voluntary, the maximum length of supervision is two and one-half years; but if the committment was by relatives or the court, the addict can be kept under supervision for seven years. This can be extended to ten years if the addict has a relapse.

Out-patients must also submit to tests utilizing "Nalline," a synthetic anti-narcotic which causes abrupt withdrawal symptoms if a person has returned to narcotics. The program provides halfway houses for use by some patients. Thus far, the program has been fairly successful, though substantially less than half of the patients have remained free of drugs.

New York has the greatest addiction problem in the nation.

With an estimated 50,000 to 100,000 addicts, the need for treatment is clear. A massive program was begun in 1967, with 250 million dollars spent the first year and anticipated annual carrying charges of 40 to 50 million dollars.

New York's Addiction Service Agency is based on programs developed by Dr. Efren Ramirez in Puerto Rico. The program consists of three phases, known as "The Concept." The first phase involves motivating addicts to go through withdrawal, then accomplishing that withdrawal. The second phase is built around participation in a therapeutic community for six to eight months, then gradual reintroduction to the community is considered the final phase.

ASA is divided into two divisions, prevention and rehabilitation. Rehabilitation is mainly accomplished through several "Phoenix Houses." Members must restrain from drugs and violence. Ex-addicts are used heavily. Group encounter sessions are held three times a week and seminars are held daily.

The prevention program is extensive, with everything from juvenile groups for potential users to various community action programs. Adults are educated in ways their attitudes may have contributed to their children's use of drugs. Local prevention and referral centers are located throughout the city.

The programs such as ASA give a glimpse of hope that we can successfully prepare the addict for productive, drug-free life. Addiction is not the end of the road. There are ways to get the monkey off the back, ways of which we need to be aware. Redemption may happen. A man can learn to accept himself as God has accepted him, and in that acceptance there is the greatest "high" in the world.

7

LEGAL ASPECTS
OF DRUG ABUSE

(By Phil Strickland)

The teenager named Freddy has a lot of time to think these days. He remembers his high school days. The memories are good, for Freddy did well in high school. His academic record was excellent, he had lettered in two sports, and his writing for the school paper had shown real talent.

Now Freddy sits in a small, lonely cell. He is nineteen years old. After graduation, Freddy was asked to spend a few days in Florida on vacation. Some of his campus friends asked him if he would mind taking some items to acquaintances who lived near Freddy's destination. They informed him that there was a small amount of marijuana concealed in one of the suit cases. The marijuana was being sent as a gift.

With some reluctance, Freddy agreed to take the luggage to Florida. Narcotic agents, acting on a tip-off, arrested him on his way to Florida. The charge was simple possession of marijuana. At the trial it was established by unrefuted testimony that Freddy himself was not a user. He was just doing a favor for friends. Nonetheless, he was found guilty and sentenced to twenty years. Now the promising young scholar and athlete spends his days visiting with hardened criminals and wondering about a society that would judge him in the way it did.

The story of Freddy is a tragic one. Sending him to jail for 20 years for carrying some marijuana from one friend to another is not justice. But Freddy's case is not that exceptional. In Texas, Gary also sits alone in his cell. He was a college student twenty-two years old when he went out with Mary Jane. He got caught, and he is now serving a ten year sentence. Nancy, a young woman in another state, is serving fifteen years for simple possession.

A host of other examples might be given. Felony convictions have even been given to teenagers for being in a house where marijuana was being used. Most people would agree that a system which would permanently damage, by a felony conviction, the life of a youngster for so minor a sin is certainly less than just. Young people, seeing such examples, become convinced that the law cannot be respected.

What are the laws that allow such incidents to occur? Do they need to be changed? These are crucial questions, both for the adult and the young person. It is in terms of legalization that many of the broader questions about drugs are being asked. "Legalize pot" is more than a statement of social policy. It is also a statement of conviction concerning the individual and social effects of using the drug. In a sense, then, the question of the legal status of drugs is the door through which one often must go to get to the other issues.

At least a basic knowledge of the law, therefore, is important for the one who desires to understand and relate to the drug culture.

What Are the Basic Laws?

The Federal criminal law which deals with narcotics and dangerous drugs is a hodge-podge of statutes that have been devised primarily to meet social emergencies. Two basic sets of laws exist—one controlling "narcotic drugs" and marijuana, the other regulating the use of "dangerous drugs."

The Federal Narcotic and Marijuana Laws

The term "narcotic drugs" includes opium and all of its derivatives such as heroin and morphine; coca leaves and its derivatives, principally cocaine; and the "opiates," defined synthetic narcotic drugs. Cocaine is inappropriately classified since it is a stimulant rather than a narcotic. Marijuana, a hallucinogen, is also misclassified with the narcotic drugs.

The Narcotic Import and Export Act was the first of the significant narcotic laws. Passed in 1909, the law authorizes the import of crude opium and coca leaves for scientific and medicinal purposes. It prohibits the fraudulent or knowing importation of other narcotics. The Act provides that "possession shall be deemed sufficient evidence to authorize conviction unless the defendant explains the possession to the satisfaction of the jury." The Act also provides a rigid system of controls to assure that only drugs to be used for medical needs are exported.

The Harrison Narcotic Act was passed in 1914. It contains the basic criminal offenses dealing with transactions in narcotics. The Act makes it unlawful to sell, exchange, or give away narcotics except with a written order of the purchaser or receipt of an official treasury order form. A first offense carries a minimum sentence of 5 years, a maximum of 20, and a maximum fine of $20,000. A second offense receives a penalty of 10 to 40 years in prison with a possible $20,000 fine. Possession penalties are 2 to 10 years for first offense, 5 to 20 years for second offense and 10 to 40 years for third and subsequent offenses. Probation and suspension of sentence are not allowed on first offense. The law does not allow suspended sentence or probation. Penalties for a person over 18 providing narcotics to one under 18 are more severe. A registration and taxation system for all persons who import, manufacture, produce or sell narcotic drugs is provided. Graduated occupational taxes are imposed.

The Marijuana Tax Act, which became law in 1937, sets forth several offenses related to marijuana. It is important to note that the same penalties and restrictions on suspended sentences and probation apply to marijuana as they do to the narcotic drugs. While it is known as a tax act, there are few legitimate transactions in it, thus it is almost entirely a criminal law. The Act provides that transfers must be pursuant to a written order or official treasury form.

No substantial medical, scientific or sociological evidence was heard in the Congressional hearings on the bill. The measure was passed rapidly and without adequate deliberation. This became evident on May 19, 1969, when the Supreme Court, in an 8–0 vote, struck down certain sections of the Marijuana Tax Act. Two sections were found to be defective: a section which presumed that a person with foreign-grown marijuana in his possession knows that it is smuggled, and a section which requires payment of taxes on the drug, which could not be done without self-incrimination in violation of the Fifth Amendment.

The Narcotics Manufacturing Act of 1960 deals primarily with manufacturers of narcotic drugs. A system of licensing is established, along with a method of determining and controlling quotas of both synthetic and natural narcotic drugs.

The last important narcotics legislation is the 1966 Narcotic

Addict Rehabilitation Act. This Act reflects the desire to rehabilitate addicts instead of just punishing them. The Act provides for treatment of three groups; addicts who have committed Federal offenses, addicts who will accept civil committment in lieu of prosecution, and civilly committed addicts who are not charged with any offense. After-care programs are provided for addicts who have been treated, and makes parole available to all marijuana violaters who have been or will be convicted under Federal law.

The Federal Dangerous Drug Laws

There is only one basic piece of legislation dealing with dangerous drugs. It is known as the Drug Abuse Control Amendments of 1965. The Amendments were amended again in 1968. This legislation is designed to control three groups of dangerous drugs—depressants, stimulants and hallucinogens such as LSD, DMT, STP, mescaline and peyote. The Attorney-General is given authority to add drugs when they possess "a potential for abuse" because of "depressant or stimulant effects on the central nervous system" or "hallucinogenic effects." Under this authority, more than 2000 drugs have been added to the controlled list.

Anyone who possesses dangerous drugs illegally is subject to a penalty of not more than one year imprisonment and/or a fine of not more than $1000. The second offense is the same. The penalty for third offense is three years imprisonment and/or a $10,000 fine. When there is possession with intent to sell or actual sale of dangerous drugs, the penalty is not more than five years imprisonment and/or a $10,000 fine. It should be noticed that these penalties, which include LSD, are substantially lower than the penalties for marijuana.

The Drug Abuse Control Amendments also seek to control drugs by regulating manufacture and distribution. Manufacturers and wholesalers must be registered, and they are required to keep specific inventories and records. The filling and refilling of prescriptions is also controlled.

As of this writing, Congress has under consideration a new "Controlled Dangerous Substances Act." A "Uniform State Controlled Dangerous Substances Act" has also been recommended. These are major new legislative proposals which would supersede previous narcotic and dangerous drug laws. The Act would set up a new classification system and give the Attorney-General power to reclassify drugs as new information became available. Extensive record keeping is required. Possession penalties for marijuana are more reasonable, and first offender treatment is provided. The provision is badly needed as over 98% of possession arrests are for first offenses. A continuing criminal enterprise provision contains extremely strict penalties.

State Laws

Some states have had drug legislation on the books since the early 1900's. But the laws had minimal sentences and were loosely enforced. In 1937, however, the Uniform Narcotics Act was recommended and since then all states have adopted the Act or a modified form of it. Many states have also adopted legislation for dangerous drugs similar to the Federal controls.

All states now have anti-marijuana laws, based generally on the Uniform Narcotics Act. Penalties tend to be very severe.

Most states still have possession penalties which range from five years to life. Some states also refuse to allow probation, parole and suspended sentences. However, a number of states have recently seen fit to either reduce the penalty for possession of marijuana from a felony to a misdemeanor, or give the judge the discretion of reducing it. Alaska, in 1968, became the first state to put marijuana under the dangerous drug laws instead of the narcotic laws. The effect was to make the penalties on marijuana similar to those for LSD and other hallucinogens.

What Needs to be Done?

The discussion of what needs to be done to our present drug laws primarily centers around one drug, marijuana. There are other areas that need change, but in most of them there is fairly general agreement on what should be done. In the area of pot laws, however, there is great contention. "Marijuana should be legalized," is the cry of many, while others are yelling, "Sock it to them." In one recent poll of candidates for state office in Texas, the question was asked, "Do you favor reduction of the penalty for first-time possession of marijuana to a misdemeanor?" Fifty-one per cent answered yes, forty-nine per cent said no.

There is a growing consensus, however, among those who deal closely with marijuana, that the present penalties are not good. Youngsters cannot understand getting zero to ten years for manslaughter, zero to ten years for selling to the enemy, and five to life for possession of marijuana.

Prosecutors and juries seem to have the same difficulty. In 1967 there were approximately 37,500 marijuana arrests in California. Three-fourths of the cases were dismissed without trial. Federal records indicate that arrests for marijuana violations totaled over 80,000 in 1968. Most were never prosecuted. Dr. Cohen of the National Institute of Mental Health has estimated that only about one per cent of those arrested on marijuana charges are brought to trial and convicted. Most, of course, are never caught.

Young people are aware of these facts. While they know that there is the possibility of getting convicted on a felony charge, they realize that the odds are tremendously in their favor. Consequently, they neither fear nor respect the law as it is.

The need for change has been recognized by our last three presidents. President Kennedy's Advisory Commission on Narcotic and Drug Abuse recommended lighter sentences for possession, as did President Johnson's Commission on Law Enforcement and the Administration of Justice. The legislation promoted by the present administration also recommends a lessening of possession penalties.

The question is, how far should we go in lessening penalties for possession? Should it be completely legalized?

Those who advocate such a policy usually make three assertions. First, there is the argument that marijuana is less harmful than alcohol. What marijuana? What alcohol? And what dosage of each? To argue on the basis of such a comparison is difficult. It is probably possible to find some marijuana which is weaker than some type of alcoholic beverage. It is also possible to find marijuana which is much more powerful than any alcoholic beverage.

The assertion is also made that it is impossible to control the use of marijuana. Law, it is pointed out, has not worked as an effective deterrent. Obviously, there is a great deal of truth in the argument. Our laws have not worked well. But, one cannot expect laws, which are unenforced because they are so excessive, to work well. It is obvious that law alone cannot control the use of marijuana. It is but one contributor to a long list of social influences. But it does contribute.

Finally, it is often asserted that people should be free to do as they please, so long as they do not hurt others. It is inappropriate for government to try to regulate what mature adults do in private. Nor can the government enforce regulations over private behavior unless they completely invade the sanctity of the home. The argument is appealing. But is it realistic to assume that it could be legalized only for use which is performed in a vacuum of privacy?

The present restrictions on marijuana indicate that society still has serious hesitations about the possible costs of social approval. To legalize it, even with restrictions, would be to say that we have resolved those hesitations and are ready to say that marijuana is innocuous. Soon, however, the synthetic material will be available and it will be possible to take as large a dose as one desires. Inevitably, there will be many people who will progress to larger and larger amounts. It is already abundantly clear that in such large doses, marijuana is a dangerous drug.

Dr. Ungerleider emphasizes the importance of knowing the "risk factor" before we put the stamp of social approval on any drug. There is much we do not know about the risk factor of marijuana. In the ordinary dose of a marijuana cigarette, the risk factor may be low. It may not. In higher doses, the risk factor appears to be substantial.

Nor can the cost to society be ignored. Society pays a significant cost for those who use marijuana so excessively that they become social derelicts. Public and private resources have to be utilized for their medical and social care. The limited medical and social care facilities and personnel are made unavailable for others. And society loses the talent of those who choose to escape rather than confront the real world.

Surely society has the right and the responsibility of limiting its escape mechanisms and intoxicants. If so, there would seem to be ample evidence that our society lacks the health to shoulder the burden of another intoxicant with unknown consequences. Laws do need to be changed. Pot penalties need to be made workable. But it is not time to assume the unknown risk factor of legalized marijuana.

8

HOW WE CAN FIGHT
THE DRUG MENACE

(By Phil Strickland)

People are important! This is a message which dwells at the heart of the Good News. In a computerized, technological age, the individual is significant. In the midst of a population explosion which sees the birth of 200 children each minute in the developing countries (40 will die in the first year) the Christian proclamation is that each one is valuable in the eyes of God. And, in a bare, cellar room with needles, eyedroppers and blank stares, there are those for whom Christ died.

The Magnitude of the Problem

It is tempting, perhaps, for one to become frustrated with the magnitude of our problems. Frustration leads to despair and despair leads to escapism. For some, escapism means drugs. For others, ignoring the drug problem is a kind of escape from reality. As the use of drugs has spread rapidly, it has become increasingly difficult to turn our backs on it, particularly when it is our parents and our children who are "hooked." The call for action is being heard. There is an increasing willingness on the part of many to "get where the action is." But, what kind of action is needed? What can be done to fight the drug menace?

The Necessity for Patience

The roots of increasing drug use are deeply embedded in our society. For years we have been creating a "pill for every pain" culture. Annually, millions of dollars are spent to incessantly bombard us with drug promises and stimuli. A host of pressures cause the psychological and sociological alienation of our youth. Together, these factors present a formidable barrier to effective communication and education.

Such barriers will not be broken down immediately. The battle against drug abuse will not be won by quick and decisive victories. Rather, it will be won by people who have the patience and wisdom to lay good foundations and build upon them.

The Clarification of the Issue

The drug menace has been so glamorized that many think the battle is against the drugs themselves. It is not. The battle is against that which causes devient behavior. The distinction is important. If we assume that the center of the problem is drugs, then our primary efforts are directed at controlling the use of drugs. This becomes a massive problem, for almost any drug is subject to abuse. Even common food items can be misused. One youth recently reported that he got a real kick out of mainlining peanut butter. He did not get many kicks. His body was not able to take but a few doses of mainlined peanut butter.

If, however, drug abuse is considered just one response to deeper tensions, then our efforts must also be directed to that which causes the tensions. It was thought for years that the drug problem was prevalent only in the lower socio-economic groups. Suddenly, however, it became obvious that the new drug subculture of the 60's had major support in youth from economically upper and upper-middle class families. This opened a whole new bag of questions. What are the frustrations of a 17-year-old boy who drives a Mustang, takes his good-looking girl to the best restaurant, then "drops some acid"? Such frustrations must be understood before there can be any successful answer to his use of the drugs.

Some Essential Elements

Several important elements must co-exist in any productive response to drug abuse. First, an effective response must be motivated by genuine concern rather than fear. Many adults find this particularly difficult when a youngster has long hair and shaggy clothes. Often, they react with fear and rejection, rather than with Christian affirmation of that person's value. Such a reaction may further alienate a youngster and make him closed for any effective ministry.

Secondly, the response should tend to de-glamorize rather than glamorize the use of drugs. Today, smoking a weed is the "cool, hip, stud, in" thing to do. To the extent that it "blows the mind" of the non-user, it is even cooler. But if, through calm communications, the non-user begins to realize that Tom is using the "uppers" because he has certain "deep-seated neurotic characteristics, tending toward psychosis, because of maladjustment to his primary environmental factors," it does something to the cool. Then, he is far more likely to say, "Tom can't face reality," than to say, "Man, Tom is really a neat guy."

A Coordinated Effort

Finally, it should be noted that any successful response to the drug menace must be fought on many fronts. The family must instill an understanding of personal worth, a sense of being loved. The church must effectively communicate the ultimate value and purpose of life. The schools must disseminate the facts, and the community must educate and control. Only as all of these elements of society form a coordinated thrust will the barriers to understanding be overcome.

The Response of the Home

The easiest place to win the battle against drug abuse is in the home. Studies have frequently shown that hard-core addicts seldom come from stable, loving homes. There are exceptions, however, and one who has a good family life should be careful not to say, "It could never happen in our home." In such a case, the problem is ignored and the tendency to become an "exception" increases. The concerned parent should give some thought and attention to at least two aspects of the relationship between parent and children.

Example. Two case histories illustrate the impact that example can have. Jim grew up watching Mom and Dad use every kind of drug imaginable. His mother used tranquillizers to get to sleep and pep pills to wake up. In between, she popped a steady stream of pills ranging from diet pills to aspirin. Whenever she faced unpleasant situations, she headed for the medicine cabinet. If she did not find a pill that would end her pain, frustration, or whatever, she would go to the next-door neighbor to get one. Usually, she did not have the faintest notion what effects the medication would really have on her. Jim's father seldom used pills. A couple of cocktails were far more relaxing. He had long ago discovered that if his problems got bad, he could drink just a few more cocktails and get relief. Cigarettes were also relaxing to him. He was aware of the possibility of lung cancer and other health problems, but he was sure such things could not happen to him. Besides, enjoy life while you can.

Jim's parents were very shocked to discover that he was mainlining heroin. A few marijuana cigarettes smoked to relieve some of the frustrations of growing up had started it. He soon discovered that if the problems got worse, a little stronger drug would bring relief.

Jim's parents said they did not know what would cause Jim to do such a thing.

Darla was a sensitive girl. Her parents seldom used drugs, with the exception of moderate use of alcohol. Darla was given the best of everything. She went to fine schools, was given a car when she was able to drive and had charge accounts in the finest stores. She was never asked to assume responsibility for any family affairs. Her mother found great enjoyment in social affairs. Her father enjoyed traveling and golf. They had a nice Negro maid who came twice a week.

Darla went away to college. She began to hear about pollution, the population explosion, racism, poverty, and war. She learned about politics and self-interest. Soon, she began to conclude that folks in this country simply do not care about people. It was easy to want to escape from that kind of world, and she soon discovered a way to do so.

Darla's parents were equally amazed to discover that their daughter had a drug problem. They had given her everything. Everything, that is, except an understanding of caring and committment.

Such case histories illustrate the tremendous importance of family example that speaks to the youngster about reasonable, discriminate use of drugs and about positively relating oneself to the needs of people. But example may not be enough in itself. A second matter is deeply important.

Communication. This is the age of the quick lunch, the school social, the club meeting, the church committee and friends over for bridge. Life is becoming increasingly crowded. The pressures of school are growing and the opportunities for recreation are myriad. In the midst of this, the family visit has become a novelty rather than a practice.

Communicating with and knowing each other now takes conscious effort. The family must seek opportunity to be together. But even togetherness does not imply communication. An evening with the "tube" may create no significant new family understanding. Such understanding is deeply needed. Growing up is at least as hard as it used to be and the youngster needs the guidance and control of his parents.

The context of communication is important. The loosely structured home with no real authority figure will not tend to promote closeness and communication. Among drug users, the complaint is often heard that parents do not set limits or prohibit any activities. Thus, there is no support from the home for the one who does not want to bow to the drug pressures exerted by his peers. The home environment must also communicate trust and acceptance. Many young people who are using drugs desperately want help but are afraid that discovery will alienate them from parents they love and do not want to hurt. The parent must communicate a love that will overcome this fear.

Communicating about drugs can be particularly sensitive. Attempts to do so often become Exhibit A in the generation gap. Emotions are high and facts are few. "Mom, I like grass" is too often the beginning of hysteria, not discussion. Real communication must begin with calmness and facts. Parents must know what they are talking about. The peer group pressures on youth are for drug acceptance in many instances. Therefore, the youngster often is just hunting an excuse to reject his parents' advice. If he can find one misstated fact he may reject the whole argument. Young people, on the other hand, need to realize the immaturity of such reactions and listen to and evaluate their parent's advice.

The Response of the Church

The church is a place for those who have made mistakes and need the message of forgiveness. Therefore, it has a crucial role to play in fighting the drug menace. It is a dual role: first, to perform a preventive ministry; second, to perform a healing ministry for those who have made mistakes with drugs.

Preventive Ministries

Special programs. One of the most obvious opportunities the church has is to conduct special drug education programs. The unique opportunity is that of conducting such programs with the whole family present. Parents and children can learn together and this provides the impetus for further discussion in the family. The programs must be carefully prepared. Knowledgeable persons should be brought in to conduct seminars. If drug education is not a part of the public school curriculum, the church should consider extensive drug education rather than just one-shot programs.

Outlet for service. The church should be just the place for the young person in search of a cause. If he is looking for something to do, a place to make his life count, the church should be prepared to help him. Telling him to go witness is not enough, for the young person of today is looking for a place to show his concern as well as speak it. He wants to go where there is human need—the ghetto, the poor, the sick, the hungry. It is incomprehensible that some churches frown on such "social involvements." How does a church discourage ministries of love when they serve Him who is love?

Often, the best deterrent to drug use is to get involved in the fight against it. Interested youth in a church, with adult guidance, can be mobilized into a task force to minister to the drug problem in their community.

Supportive role. The church should be careful not to duplicate other efforts. A program does not have to originate in the church to be worthwhile. The church should stand ready to lend its resources, especially financial, to educational and community efforts. It should also encourage the development of other efforts that are needed. This "catalyst" role can often be very productive.

Pastoral counseling. There have been some interesting studies which indicate that drug experimenters are generally reluctant to talk to pastors, even when they feel in need of help. Two reasons are frequently mentioned. First, there is a lack of faith that the pastor has any real understanding of the drug scene. Secondly, there is the feeling that the minister's response will be more one of condemnation than of empathy. Surely, these indictments do not apply to all pastors. They should, however, cause the pastor to examine his own role and be prepared for it. He should, for example, carefully think through his response to the fact that his counselee is violating the law. He may even be a minor pusher who wants to break the habit. What should his response be in such a case? If he is prepared, the pastor can have a significant impact in his counseling time.

Healing Ministries

The referral ministry. If the minister or others in the church are dealing with an addict, they almost certainly need help. It should be the responsibility of someone in the church to be aware of the local, state and national facilities for rehabilitation.

No meaningful progress can be made (except in rare cases) while the addict is controlled by drugs. So, the first task is to get him to accept physical withdrawal. Deciding to do so can be difficult for an addict, so the pastor may have to be directive in his counseling. Generally, the addict will then need specialized treatment. Some of the possibilities for such treatment were mentioned in a previous chapter.

The support ministry. When an addict comes back from treatment, he has little hope of making it unless he can find help and acceptance from those who are "straight." His immediate need is a place to stay as he readjusts to society. Next, he needs a job. This can be a serious problem, for finding work for a former addict is not an easy task. Finally, he needs a new set of relationships and he needs them immediately. If he does not find them quickly, he will go back to the only relationships he knows —with users. The church has the resources to meet all three of these needs. Others may provide jobs or a temporary place to live, but seldom are they ready to provide lasting relationship. Here the church has unique opportunity.

The family ministry. Usually, one of the crucial needs of the addict is to be realigned to his family. Usually, feelings of separation are part of the motivation for drug use. Thus it is important to help the family rebuild bridges of relationship. Also, an addict in the family may precipitate other crises. Husband and wife wonder who failed and begin to blame each other. The value system of the family may be thrown into chaos. "Why did it happen to my son" will be disturbing them. All of these factors create a situation where the forgiveness and support of fellow-Christians is deeply needed.

The counseling ministry. The counselor can perform an important rehabilitative as well as preventive role. When an addict returns home, he needs to be responsible to someone. Like an adolescent, he needs limits set for him. He needs an authority figure, one who will detect it when he slips back to drugs, and who will also be able to empathize and help him through periods of frustration.

An outstanding example of effective church involvement is the Narcotics Committee of East Harlem Protestant Parish. The parish is privately financed and provides numerous services to the community as well as providing worship facilities. There is an advisory board which includes representatives from a number of Protestant groups.

One of the services provided is the Narcotics Committee. Included on the committee are a number of professional people. There is a staff which has offices and facilities in the parish. Among the services offered are help in withdrawal, referral to hospitals, and legal advice. Also, addicts returning from treatment are given help in finding jobs, food, clothing, and nondrug companionship. Counseling, for both the addict and family, is included. Spiritual guidance is emphasized.

This is just one example of the creative ministry the church can have. Many more are needed.

The Response of the Schools

Most observers share the conviction that real drug education has not been tried in this country. The educational institutions have been slow to respond to the rapid increase in drug experimentation. Even now, only a few school systems are beginning to include drug education in various parts of the regular curriculum. Some states have passed legislation directing their departments of education to develop curriculum materials for regular drug courses. In many places, however, local citizens need to communicate their desire for drug programs to local school boards and to their state representatives. Local school boards should be requested to implement special programs until materials can be developed, then to include such materials as a regular part of the curricula.

It is, of course, impossible to go into detail concerning program possibilities in the few paragraphs available here. Besides, there are many variables that can only be considered on the local level. Mention can be made, however, of some of the more basic considerations of a minimum drug education program. While this is done with a school program primarily in mind, the observations generally apply to other educational efforts.

The first question that must be discussed is when such education should begin. There is growing sentiment for beginning it in the elementary grades. Here, drug education would be included in the broader subject of good health practices. Discussion would be concerned with taking things from medicine cabinets, sniffing fumes from substances like gasoline, and similar matters. Drug education should probably continue through high school, with some full courses directed to the subject in the later years. There are dissenters to this view who argue that detailed instruction will increase interest which will, in turn, lead to increased drug behavior. The interest, however, already exists and it is difficult to see where a more adequate understanding would lead to a less discriminate use.

A second question which arises, particularly in relation to the more advanced classes, concerns what will be taught. The answer depends on the needs and backgrounds of the students, as well as the goal sought. For example, if the goal is to eliminate all nonmedical use of drugs, then the negative case concerning alcohol and cigarettes must be stressed. If the goal is discriminate use, the approach will be different. If the audience is composed of mostly nonusers, then presenting the basic facts might be sufficient. If, however, the audience includes a large number of users or "heads," more sophisticated in drugs, then the material will also have to be more sophisticated.

Another important consideration is the problem of selecting teachers and lecturers. Caution must be exercised that whomever is chosen is adequately acquainted with the material. Unlike many subjects, there is advanced status in being more knowledgable about drugs than your peers. Consequently, many youngsters have developed a great deal of expertise, either through experience or interest. It is imperative, therefore, that the teacher be extremely well-prepared in the subject material.

Finally, attention must be given to how the materials will be presented. The main problem is not the material, but in getting students to believe what the material states. Because many students have, or think they have, a certain amount of understanding of the subject, discussion can be a very effective technique. Former addicts can also be very provocative. Caution must be used, for there are some former addicts who still need the drug status, so they tend to glorify the drug experience they once had. There are many, however, who out of their experience are deeply dedicated to helping others avoid the tragic life of the addict. Their testimony is often one of the most effective ways to deglamorize the whole drug experience.

Advantage should be taken of the many excellent visual aids that are already available. Although there is little textbook material, literature can be received from the World Health Organization, the Bureau of Narcotics and Dangerous Drugs, the United States Public Health Service, the American Medical Association and other organizations, as well as from local police and medical sources. The literature should be examined before use. Some of it tends to sensationalism that is not often effective with young people.

The Response of the Community

Community efforts can add a valuable assist in the battle against drug abuse. Often, it is a concerned community program which first brings local problems to the attention of the people. This, in turn, may precipitate home, church and school responses. In addition, there are some things the community effort can uniquely accomplish. Adults and parents will not be taking drug courses in the school. The church will reach few of them with educative programs. So the only hope of reaching most adults with information concerning the drug culture is through community efforts.

Another area in which a community effort is usually necessary is in drug rehabilitation. Additional rehabilitation centers have long been needed. Even smaller communities may need to provide out-patient care for those who return from rehabilitation clinics in other cities.

A number of community programs across the country have been quite successful. When one looks closely at these programs, he discovers that they have several characteristics in common. First, the successful programs had the support of community leaders. Bank presidents, lawyers, educators, doctors, and other leading citizens were enlisted at the very first. This pretty well assured community backing and funding of the programs.

Secondly, support was enlisted from as many organizations as possible. In Roslyn, Long Island, for example, representatives of some fifty civic, religious, school and service organizations got together for an initial conference on the drug problem. Law enforcement agencies are generally sympathetic and their support should be enlisted.

Another common factor among the successful programs was the use of young people. It is extremely important that young people be allowed to help in planning and strategy. There is generation-gap enough without widening it with programs which turn off the young people. To bridge that gap, it is necessary to have the advice of the youngsters.

Finally, each of the programs set some fairly definite, reasonable and obtainable goals. For one community it was to set up a ranch treatment center. In another case the goal was to stimulate adult awareness and provide every family with a minimum number of facts and the opportunity for further study.

The innumerable possibilities of utilizing the mass media are just beginning to be explored. The National Institute of Mental Health has begun a very level-headed information campaign in the mass media. One of their ads pictures a litter of cocktail glasses, overflowing ash trays, and empty pill bottles, then asks parents; "Ever wonder why your kid doesn't take you seriously when you lecture him about drugs?" This sort of utilization of the mass media must take place on the community level as well as nationwide.

People are important, important enough to demand our utmost effort to help them confront the realities of this day. What has been suggested in this chapter is just a beginning. Many young people have decided to escape from a world which they think does not care. But we have a great opportunity to show them some people do care—by caring for them.

A SUGGESTION

The problem of drug abuse is a terrible menace to our culture. As a reader of this book, you are probably among those persons in our country who have genuine ability to form opinions and take actions. If you have found this book helpful, may we suggest that you consider:

· Using this book as a basis for study groups in your church, club, or school—

· Placing copies in your church or public library.

The publishers would appreciate any comment you have concerning this book. Please write:

Broadman Press
127 9th Avenue North
Nashville, Tennessee 37203